DEFUSING EXPLOSIVE BEHAVIOR IN CHILDREN WITH ADHD

PEACEFUL PARENTING STRATEGIES TO IDENTIFY TRIGGERS TEACH SELF-REGULATION AND CREATE STRUCTURE FOR A DRAMA-FREE HOME

ROSE LYONS

CONTENTS

Free for you!

As a thank you for reading this book, download this BONUS GUIDE to teach your child how to keep their room tidy and functional in 7 steps!

Check out my other books and follow me on Amazon to get updates of when I have new publications! Click here to Follow Me Rose Lyons Author Page

Join our Community!

Hosted by Author
Rose Lyons

A PRIVATE COMMUNITY TO GET THE SUPPORT YOU ARE LOOKING FOR

This is the beginning of your exciting journey with your child! If you'd like more awesome content and support from other parents just like you, then I invite you to join the Parenting a Child with ADHD Facebook Community

I dedicate this book to my amazing family who have been nothing but supportive. My kids are my inspiration for wanting to help more parents in navigating their path of parenting children with ADHD. And a huge thank you to my husband who has believed in me and continued to push me when things got hard. I love you all.

INTRODUCTION

If you are patient in one moment of anger, you will escape a hundred days of sorrow.

— CHINESE PROVERB

Being diagnosed with a neurodivergent disorder like ADHD opens the door to various challenges, especially for children who are still dependent. ADHD is not, however, a sign that someone is broken. Rather than attempt to fix it, it is in your child's best interest to focus on managing their disorder and becoming the best version of who they already are.

A couple of years back, I was at a parent-teacher meeting on behalf of my daughter when a child who looked about the age of six suddenly entered the room, her eyes searching for her parents. She seemed upset about something, and as soon as her eyes landed on her mother, she threw a fit and yelled at the top of her lungs, explaining how a classmate had taken her pencil case. The child was experiencing an outburst, and when her mother tried to soothe her by getting down to her level to speak with her, the child screamed. Her mother made other attempts to rein in her daughter's outburst, but it was to no avail. The child was determined to say everything she had to without any awareness of the environment. Moreover, based on her mother's embarrassed expression, it appeared this wasn't a first-time incident.

When a child has ADHD, their behavioral patterns can stress out family members, especially the parents. Your child's symptoms may vary from mild to extreme, depending on the severity of the disorder. Every parent loves their child and will always have their best interests at heart, but regardless of this honest intention, parenting children with ADHD can seem frustrating and make you question the depth of your love for them.

You are not alone. This is a familiar feeling of anxiety among parents of children with ADHD. Often, your child may have emotional outbursts, breakdowns, fits of anger, and moments of depression. These are events, amongst many others, that you have been unable to manage appropriately. It is understandable because children with ADHD can be challenging. It is not your fault, and it is not your child's fault, either. Your child's behavior is not an attempt to push your buttons to the extreme, nor is it a result of something you did wrong as a parent.

Children with ADHD should not be written off as children with unsolvable behavioral issues, as they can grow to become successful individuals in society. You will have numerous struggles as you go through life's hurdles with your children who have ADHD. But it would help if you always thought about this analogy. You know how your dog gets so excited because you enter the room? Be that way with your child. Show them that you are excited to see them and show them attention. Doing this will help them know how much you care and are there for them. Your love and support of your children, even in the most challenging moments, will help shape them into successful individuals. There are many incredible stories of children with ADHD growing up and succeeding in their lives, and all those troubles they had as a kid has subsided. For example, Olympic swimmer and gold medalist Michael Phelps grew up with ADHD. His symptoms included anxiety and behavioral issues. He was inattentive and would grab papers from his classmates. Some people in his entourage even said that he'd never amount to anything. Thankfully his mother advocated for him, and despite his challenges, he found passion and success. Having a child with ADHD does not mean they cannot become amazing members of society. We are focusing on the approach to help them get there.

Understandably, as a parent, you are at that point in your life where you'd like to know that there is hope to get through each hurdle of this parenting marathon, which sometimes leaves you feeling disheartened. It would help if you had all the pointers and practical solutions to alleviate your problems with managing your child and restoring balance to all that has been out of proportion in your relationship. This book provides many possible answers to your questions and gives you a deeper understanding of your child's struggles with their emotions and how much you need to be a safe space for them as a parent. We are especially focusing on children who experience explosive behavior as part of their ADHD symptoms to assist parents with defusing these behaviors before they occur and how to handle them during. However, the book can also be used by any parent with ADHD children as a tool to add to their parenting toolbox.

The book further explores concrete solutions to modify your parenting methods and prevent you from constantly feeling on edge with your children. Children with ADHD need parents who lead by example and help them manage behaviors through principles rather than uncontrolled emotions.

Leading by example can be extremely helpful to your children's development.

It is important to remember that you are human, too, and your children need to see you being accountable for your actions. So if you were to lose your cool and snap or yell at your child, apologize.

I have compiled factual information through experience with two incredibly beautiful and energetic ADHD-diagnosed children and intensive study of this disorder of others for over fifteen years. I aim to help parents better deal with and manage children's behaviors with this diagnosis while negotiating the challenges of running a family and career. The knowledge in this book represents my foray into sharing with parents who need expertise and support to raise great children irrespective of their disorder.

Before discovering new information, successfully parenting children with ADHD was extremely difficult. There was no guide or support, and parenting was mostly done through guesswork and the hopes that one was making the right decisions. However, the emergence of new findings and solutions alleviates the uncertainties and mental pressure of parenting children with ADHD. So, rest assured; I can guide you through this turbulent stage of parenting by sharing personal experiences you will find relatable and proven solutions you can rely on.

1
———

DEMYSTIFYING ADHD

WHAT IS ADHD?

Attention-deficit/hyperactivity disorder (ADHD) is a chronic medical disorder that includes persisting behavioral problems like acting on impulse, being hyperactive, and having difficulty sustaining attention. Many children have this disorder, and they may continue to manage it into adulthood. However, children with the disorder might experience low self-esteem, trouble sustaining relationships in the home and beyond, and poor academic performance. Your child's symptoms may decrease as they age. However, they will never wholly transition out of their ADHD symptoms and become neurotypical. Don't be alarmed, though. The disorder can be managed. Through your help and guidance, your children can learn strategies to become successful and productive individuals.

It is essential as a parent to have an in-depth understanding of what ADHD entails and to be well-equipped with information that will support the process of applying life-changing measures. For example, you might have realized that treatments can help manage symptoms but will not cure ADHD. Treatment for ADHD in children and adults typically involves medications and behavioral management interventions by professionals. However, an early diagnosis and the treatment you apply can significantly affect how your child manages ADHD.

TYPES OF ADHD

ADHD characteristics can differ according to gender, with the diagnosis occurring more often in male children than in females. Although boys usually exhibit more hyperactivity, which a disorder like ADHD can amplify, it may differ completely from girls, who are more likely to show traits of being quietly inattentive. Hyperactivity and inattentiveness are two major features of ADHD present before the age of 12. There is no stipulated age for when ADHD traits in children can appear; oftentimes, you might even find them present in a three-year-old, depending on how mild or severe the disorder may be in your child.

There are three widely known types of ADHD:

- Predominantly inattentive: Children with predominantly inattentive symptoms usually have difficulty staying focused during playtime and when performing tasks. They have trouble following simple instructions you have laid out for them, as they are easily distracted. To understand what kind of ADHD symptom is predominant in your child, look into how often they lose tools needed to perform tasks—like pencils, toys, and books—and whether they avoid tasks that require organizing and mental effort. If your child reflects these characteristics, they are predominantly inattentive. You should note that this does not mean other symptoms are not evident; they are simply minimal.
- Predominantly hyperactive/impulsive: Hyperactivity and a pattern of impulsive behavior in children can be evident when they always seem on the go, constantly moving and running around when inappropriate. Hyperactive children usually have difficulty waiting their turn and seem fidgety, tapping,

squirming, or making other body movements that imply they are unsettled. Your child may have a habit of interrupting your conversations with your partner or other people and seem to need a keen eye for when they should or should not engage, despite being old enough to understand this. In these circumstances, refrain from responding harshly since they simply do not know better.

- Combined: Some children have a mix of inattentiveness and a hyperactive or impulsive behavioral pattern. You can tell your child has a combined type of ADHD when most of the inattentive and hyperactive symptoms are evident in their behavior. That is, both types are predominant.

IS SOMETHING WRONG WITH MY CHILD?

There is absolutely nothing wrong with your child. Most children are typically inattentive, impulsive, and hyperactive in the early stages and even later in their development. Healthy children—especially preschoolers—are energetic and often full of life even after they've worn you out as a parent. For older children and teenagers, the length of their attention span during an activity solely depends on their interests.

DEMYSTIFYING ADHD | 23

Therefore, you should never classify your child as having ADHD when they are just children or because they are quite the opposite compared to their calm and reserved siblings. Your child's hyperactivity or inattentiveness could be natural, as some children are more outgoing and eager to engage in activities than others. If your child has difficulty socializing or getting along with peers in school but seems to do fine at home with their siblings, this might result entirely from something else, not necessarily ADHD.

If you ever feel overly concerned that your child may be displaying core symptoms of ADHD, you must consult your family doctor or pediatrician. Diagnosing a child with ADHD can only be done by a specialist in children's development and behavior, a psychiatrist, or a pediatric neurologist. Seeking a medical evaluation is crucial and might reveal other potential medical disorders that could explain your child's struggles and difficulties. In circumstances where a diagnosis is made, you will receive the support needed to manage your child effectively.

CAUSES OF ADHD

The causes of ADHD remain unknown, and research is ongoing. However, existing studies indicate that causes could be linked to genetics, environmental factors, or central nervous system problems during a child's essential stages of development. For example, exposure to environmental toxins like lead may influence the emergence of ADHD; this toxin can be found in older homes and buildings that contain lead pipes or lead-based paints. Other theories that could make a child more likely to have ADHD include:

- Premature birth: Children born prematurely have less time for brain development during the gestational period. This has been linked to ADHD.

- Genetics: Children who have parents, siblings, or other blood relatives with ADHD or similar mental disorders are more likely to have ADHD themselves. Chances are that one of your children will have ADHD if you or their other parent has it; the chances of inheritance are slimmer but not written off if a distant blood relative has been diagnosed.

- Alcohol and tobacco use during pregnancy: The abuse of alcohol and tobacco during pregnancy is generally bad for a child's cognitive growth and development. One of the adverse effects of abuse could be ADHD.

- The brain's anatomy: Lower activity levels in the parts of the brain regulating focus could lead to a disorder like ADHD.

ADHD in children is not caused by poor parenting or too much screen time. Unfortunately, most parents tend to believe that their poor parenting results in children's impulsive behavior or inability to pay attention or excel in academics. Another common misconception is that hyperactivity stems from consuming too much sugar or food additives, receiving immunizations, or being exposed to environmental factors such as poverty or chaos in the family. While these factors can feasibly contribute to certain behavioral patterns in children, there is no evidence that they cause ADHD.

WHAT TO EXPECT

ADHD can be an extremely difficult medical disorder for most children to manage at the early stages. If your child has been diagnosed with ADHD, you can expect the following:

- Children with ADHD often struggle in social places; they have difficulty interacting with their peers and will continually strive to find acceptance from adults and their playmates.

- They daydream a lot, which causes them to be inattentive and unable to focus for too long. Depending on the predominant symptom in your child, they might talk too much for your liking. This could be a result of being hyperactive or impulsive.
- They usually seem forgetful and confused, lose track of the order of things and situations, and have difficulty resisting temptation. This is why they might do the opposite of what you have instructed.
- They tend to have minimal self-esteem and doubt their capabilities; this may reduce their chances of succeeding if the disorder is undiagnosed or unattended.
- Teenagers who have ADHD may struggle academically or find it challenging to keep up with lessons because they are inattentive and can barely exert focus when it comes to doing assignments, studying, and performing tasks effectively.
- They are more easily prone to accidents and sustaining injuries compared to children who do not have ADHD.
- They might forget the common protective measures you taught them.

- The peak severity of hyperactivity and impulsive behavior in children with ADHD is usually at seven or eight. However, there is no age range for peak severity in children with predominantly inattentive behavior.
- Some children with ADHD can experience explosive behavior. Explosive behavior means they can experience outbursts or extreme meltdowns in the snap of a moment. It can be a result of overstimulation, frustration, or an inability to express themselves. It is an overreaction to the situation, and the correct measures must be applied to defuse it.

When unaddressed, ADHD in teenagers can lead to depression, worsen the family conflict and their relationships with others, induce stress, affect their chances of getting a job, and lead to other serious issues like substance abuse.

FAMILY LIFE FOR CHILDREN WITH ADHD

An ADHD diagnosis doesn't imply the end of your child's life. By contrast, they can always go on to lead a normal, long, and fulfilling life. But, at the same time, their behavior might make you feel they are too difficult for you to manage. After all, you are human and can become emotionally overwhelmed when your limits are tested.

Imagine you have had a long day as a caregiver performing domestic duties and are looking forward to finally getting some rest after your adolescents return from school and settle in. However, when they arrive, they will not stay put; they are everywhere, exhibiting excessive physical movement and acting without thinking. It sometimes feels almost impossible to parent them because they do not seem to be listening to you. You spent so much time trying to catch up on laundry, clean up the kitchen, maybe tidy their rooms and in a blink of an eye, it's all destroyed. This kind of situation can be exhausting to keep up with on a daily basis. However, it is possible to work on this with time and effort. When you work with your children, you can help them learn how to manage situations, make decisions, and be accountable instead of attempting to make them conform. And by doing this at home, you are also helping to set children up for success in other areas of their lives.

The behavior of children with ADHD might also impact other family members, like their siblings or your partner. Everyone will always seem to be on the lookout for them because they might be engaged in activities that could put them in physical danger. This

DEMYSTIFYING ADHD | 29

pattern of behavior can make you inadvertently shift your focus to the child with ADHD and give less attention to the other children because they aren't as hyperactive or do not demand as much attention.

The siblings may feel ignored and uncared for in such cases, causing jealousy, resentment, and hatred. As a family, the demands of monitoring a child with ADHD are exhausting and overwhelming; you always seem to be repeating the cycle of being frustrated by your child's inability to listen to instructions, snapping at them out of anger, and then feeling guilty about your harsh reaction.

When your child with ADHD has moments of explosive behavior, this can make family life even more difficult. That is why learning to defuse and deal with a situation is important for the entire family. While you need to work with your ADHD child to establish coping methods for explosive behavior to reduce it, it is also necessary to communicate with your other children so that they can understand what is happening and not fear their sibling.

Neurotypical children can be difficult enough to manage; having one or more children with ADHD under your care can be even more challenging and emotionally taxing. Their behaviors can disrupt family life and make overcoming family conflict and disorganization difficult. However, has it ever crossed your mind that your children's behavioral deficits are not intentional? Children with ADHD wish to be calm and collected, to be able to clean and tidy up their rooms, to put toys away, to function normally in social gatherings, to have high self-esteem, and to be able to listen attentively in class and excel in their academics. They simply do not know how.

When you understand that ADHD is just as frustrating and challenging for your children as it is for you as a parent, you will be one step closer to responding positively to them instead of being harsh or passively aggressive. Further, understanding how much ADHD impacts your child's future, their tendency to succeed, and the family will take you another step closer to being supportive and prepared to help them live a better lifestyle. The best kind of home for helping a child with ADHD lead a normal and successful life is one with structure, compassion, love, and a strong support system.

Even though parenting children with ADHD can be a struggle, remember to tell your kids you love them. You need to tell them you love them when they make the right decisions and even when they make the wrong decisions. Let them know that you love them on their good and bad days. Show them that you love them if they're happy and smiley, and you still love them when they are angry. Ensuring your children know that there is nothing that could ever take away the love that you feel for your kids is important. You need to tell your kids that you enjoy being around them. Ensuring you express all this love to your children is imperative because it can help them feel safe and cared for. It can also help your children know you are there for them no matter what happens. It may seem like a given to them, but words and actions are necessary to ensure your children know you love them. This is something that all children need but especially for children with ADHD who struggle in so many parts of their lives, it is vital. You are your children's rock. You are their safe haven, and they have to know that.

Family life, when you have a child or children with explosive behavior as one of their ADHD symptoms, can be even more complex. However, there are numerous ways that this behavior can be defused, and the goal of this book is to assist parents in this process. In turn, parents can work with their children on this. Building a solid foundation is the key to helping the child be successful in dealing with their ADHD and the behaviors that accompany it.

This book teaches a lot about ADHD and parenting children with this disorder. This book will focus on defusing explosive behavior in children with ADHD, although it can be a beneficial tool for anyone parenting a child with ADHD. But, if you're looking for a book to provide you with a deeper understanding of ADHD, you can also read my first book, **Parenting a Child with ADHD: How to Prepare Your Child for School Life, Integrate Executive Functioning Skills, and Foster Successful Friendships, by Rose Lyons.**

2

EMOTIONAL REGULATION

Have you ever seen a friend's child, for instance, fighting or throwing temper tantrums? Perhaps this is all new to you, and you see your friend's embarrassment when she sees you watching. She asks her daughter Becca to share her toys with your daughter who has come over for a play-date but instead the child, who was content a minute ago, takes it badly and screams at her friend, "I hate you!" You may be surprised to see such behavior in a five-year-old, especially if your child doesn't act this way. However, that is the explosive behavior typical of children with ADHD. Upon seeing such behavior played out, you might think, "oh, teach that disrespectful child some manners!" But if your friend hasn't filled you in on her child's condition, you aren't aware of all the facts and how hard the mother has probably been working with her child. What happens next between the mother and her child is a reminder that we shouldn't be judgmental towards other parents.

Your friend does not ground the girl or take away her toys. Instead, she asks Becca to come sit with her and begins singing to her. You're surprised because you've never seen such methods used when a child misbehaves. Instead, you see singing as a reward. However, like magic, Becca is calm and no longer experiencing a tantrum or destroying things and apologizes to her friend for saying something so hurtful. In your mind, you say, "what just happened?" Later, when you talk to your friend about it, she explains how Becca has ADHD, and this method is what works for her. While you have never seen these de-escalation methods, you are amazed by how well they work and are proud of your friend for her efforts to help her child in such a unique way.

Raising children is draining enough, from preparing them for school to fixing their lunch, doing their laundry, and ensuring they are prim and proper for a school day. However, think about parents who must ensure this is on track while also dealing with children with explosive behaviors. That is too many irons in the fire and could make a parent delve into phases of depression. Children with ADHD are prone to explosive behaviors as a result of the characteristics which come with the disorder. It is not uncommon to see a child with ADHD have emotional dysregulation, poor impulse control, and mood disorders. According to the Medical Director of Saranga Psychiatry in North Carolina, Vinay Saranga, some children with the disorder cannot control their emotions and have poor frustration tolerance, resulting in them lashing out (Schuck, 2022). Many parents try different coping mechanisms to manage their child's outbursts. While such methods may succeed, in many cases, it would seem as though the child in question eventually outgrows each solution.

WHAT ARE EXPLOSIVE BEHAVIORS?

In an article on explosive behaviors, Dr. Carlson concluded that explosive behavior is like a fever, a symptom of many illnesses (Carlson, 2022). You know your child is sick but cannot pinpoint their suffering. It can result from ADHD, ODD, mania, anxiety, depression, autism, and Intermittent Explosive Disorder.

Although this book focuses on explosive behavior as a symptom of ADHD, it is important to note these other psychological problems that could result in explosive behavior.

If a child has Intermittent Explosive Disorder (IED), they display sudden and extreme anger. They may also tend towards violence. These children, usually in the age bracket of late childhood to early teens, get into fights and are generally seen in the middle of some confrontation or outburst. Consequently, this affects their relationship with family and performance at school.

HOW CAN PARENTS EMPLOY EMOTIONAL REGULATION?

The ability to regulate your emotions will help you process complicated feelings without getting triggered. This skill relies on emotional intelligence, the ability to express and manage emotions and relationships. Emotional regulation allows people to avoid overreacting. While emotional regulation will help you correctly align your feelings to your goals, emotional dysregulation, as you can imagine, does the opposite.

There are methods you can employ to manage your child's temper. One method with a high success rate with explosive children is PEACE, which stands for

Pause, Emphasize, Avoid/Aware, Calm, and Expectations.

HOW CAN PARENTS USE PEACE TO REGULATE EXPLOSIVE CHILDREN?

Parents, teachers, or guardians whose children exhibit violent behavior should, first and foremost, understand that these children act in that specific way due to their disorder. It is not entirely their fault that they lash out and get physical with people and things. Research has shown that children with explosive disorders reflect on their actions and feel guilty after causing problems. Some even break down and cry, while others get confused. Here is how you can handle situations without harming your child and avoid being harmed yourself:

- Pause: Yes, pause. It is an innate characteristic in humans to counterattack when faced with violent situations, but one should understand that they are dealing with children. Stop whatever you are doing. These children only mirror what has been displayed to them by older people. You want to avoid gestures that could startle the child and not look down on them; instead, get down on their level and

maintain eye contact with them (Doddson, W.,
2022). Pausing is a valuable measure to keep
yourself from reacting immediately without
listening.

- Empathize: This method should be carried out
before or after an outburst. This serves as a self-
awareness mechanism passed from parent to
child. It would help to tell your child that
aggressiveness should not be used to escape a
difficult situation. Talk to them repeatedly
about recognizing their unique stressor and
getting themselves out of their situation. Even if
they have another outburst, keep practicing.
With time, they will learn and get better. It is
unrealistic to think they will not have another
outburst, so try to create realistic goals instead
and prepare for them.

- Aware/Avoid: You should be mindful of the
situation and avoid making things worse. Do
not raise your voice, do not tell your child you
do not care and do not shut down. However,
you should not walk away in the heat of the
moment and leave your child to deal with their
emotions alone. Be aware of how your child
does best in calming down. Do they prefer to sit
down in a corner with you in a room to
regroup? Do they prefer to sit by you and have

you hug them? Avoid arguing with or yelling at the child. Rather than resolving problems, this would only compound them and have an adverse effect. In addition, arguments distract you from the issue at hand.

- Calm: Being calm during an overwhelming situation for your child helps defuse their outburst. You must be able to listen and understand the problem. Do not belittle or write off their feelings as invalid; be careful with your language. Validate their feelings and avoid making them feel stupid. All of our emotions form who we are. According to Dr. Miller, validation means showing acceptance and being nonjudgmental, and this is important because when a child feels understood, they tend to let go of powerful negative emotions (Miller, 2022).

- Expectations: This refers to the conversations that ensue after the situation is resolved and emotions have settled. Let your children know that it is not okay to yell at people, throw things, or display other negative behaviors that may put others in danger. You may set such expectations as "I want you to come to talk to me when you are upset about something so we can figure it out together" and "It hurts my feelings when you say you hate me, so please do not say it anymore."

Every parent with an ADHD-diagnosed child should understand the PEACE strategy so they can apply it when needed.

OTHER METHODS FOR ACHIEVING EMOTIONAL REGULATION

The following list provides additional methods to help your child regulate their emotions:

- Create diversion. Please understand your child's narrative and why they act as they do, and listen to them. Knowing their narrative helps them feel heard and regain their sense of control. Ask questions but know when is the right time to ask those questions.
- Use body contact. Body contact creates an intimate relationship between people. Never underestimate how powerful a hug can be during a meltdown. You could hug your child and steady them when they have outbursts. This simple gesture could help cool their temper. This can create a negative emotion for

some children, so again, know if your child would benefit from a hug or a soft touch.

- Put emotions into words. They say evil thrives in secrecy. When a comment or activity is out in the open, its effect is reduced. Teach your children how to put their feelings into words. Whenever they feel angry, let them say, "I am angry." The difference between children who put their emotions into words and those who do not is the chaos resulting from poor communication. A child who does not tell anyone about their anger may have more outbursts than those who do. When children can vocalize their feelings, it helps to prevent violent tendencies (Hallowel, 2022).

- Using words or pictograms, work to determine what your child is feeling. Doing so may help you to pinpoint the cause of the emotions. Since experiencing regular emotions is normal for development and happens to anyone, it is a balancing act to determine if your child's reaction is due to usual emotions or emotional dysregulation. Feeling sadness and anger is just a child finding their boundaries, which is okay. When it is explosive, and the child cannot express themselves except in negative ways, there is an issue. Overall, we do not want to tell our children not to feel these things but instead teach them how to cope and manage them appropriately. Developing the right strategies to help your child manage their emotions might take time. The important thing is that you do not give up when working through their feelings.

- Reward good behavior. Parents should learn to be positive when disciplining a child. For instance, research has shown that rewarding a child for their good acts is more effective than punishing them for bad behavior. When little Becca gets cotton candy or toys for being good to her siblings, she would most likely do good things to earn rewards. However, parents should be creative in rewarding children so they do not feel entitled when doing good (Bertin, 2022).

In the end, parents and teachers need to understand that although a child will not outgrow ADHD, this disorder can be managed so that the child has healthy relationships with others. In addition, managing ADHD goes a long way in positively shaping a child's development. The difference between a child with ADHD who grows up to become a successful adult and one who throws tantrums and gets in trouble at the adult stage all boils down to how their ADHD was managed when they were younger. Therefore, parents, guardians, and teachers of children with explosive behaviors should pay attention to these children and fortify their quivers with peace arrows.

3

THE ROLE OF PARENTS

arenting a child or children with ADHD can be very challenging, and you hold a great deal of responsibility in raising them. Caring for them will seem almost impossible because they tend to engage in behavioral patterns that negate your teachings and expectations. ADHD can be managed with the right treatment and support, and you are saddled with the responsibility of helping your child manage their struggles. Your positive influence on your child makes a big difference in their academics. You assist them in acquiring important life skills and, most importantly, making family life easier to manage. It all begins with you – the caregiver. You can apply many methods to help your child become a better version of themselves. For parents of children who exhibit explosive behavior as one of their ADHD symptoms, parenting is even more difficult. There may be days when you feel like you cannot succeed, but we are here to tell you that you and your child can overcome all the hurdles you will face. In this chapter, we are going to provide you with some tips on how you can use your role as a parent to help your child while ensuring that you are caring for yourself and the rest of your family at the same time.

DEALING WITH YOUR EMOTIONS

Emotions are an integral part of human functioning. While your role is to keep the family in good shape and help your child grow into a healthy and responsible adult, it is understandable if your emotions sometimes slip out of control. Parenting a child with ADHD will test your patience, exhaust you physically, mentally, and emotionally, and might also subject you to judgment from others who assume you lack parental skills.

You must never ignore or downsize the ways circumstances impact your well-being. Instead, you should recognize that there will be moments of emotional outbursts. Finding support or strategies for dealing with emotions is imperative, so you do not inadvertently take it out on your child.

Everyone needs "me time" to detox from negative emotions and recharge for better performances. Take a break if you ever feel overwhelmed with responsibility or like you are moving at the speed of light. Ask your partner or child to pitch in with chores and errands. Participating in fun and stress-relieving activities like reading a book, soaking in the bathtub, walking, or watching your favorite TV show can help you regulate your emotions.

If you are married or in a long-term relationship with your partner, spend exclusive time out together to unwind and discuss your emotions. You can steer clear of conversations around your children and catch a break. Instead, attend events, perform yoga and mindfulness meditation, exercise often, go on vacation, have dinner together, or go on dates. At the same time, the children are in the care of a babysitter. Invest in self-care because you can only support your children when you are in the right mind.

ENACTING BEHAVIORAL CHANGE

Encouraging a shift in your child's behavior requires that you have the parental skill and knowledge to influence positive changes strategically. You can apply many methods to support behavioral change in your child's life.

Set Boundaries and Have Expectations

Rules hold great importance for humans. For example, if your community sets a rule to behead any thief caught, the crime rate will most likely decrease in the community. People fear consequences, and children are not left out of this math. They need to know what you frown at and what grants them a "well done" pat on the back, a head rub, or an extra scoop of ice cream. You must state these boundaries and expectations simply, concisely, and clearly, so your child fully understands them.

Write your rules and expectations on a poster board and fix it on a wall in a part of your house that's noticeable. The following are some examples:

- Be kind
- Pick up after yourself
- No yelling
- Do not leave your things lying around

You can write these rules and expectations in colorful letters for your child to follow. You can also add a graphic if this is helpful for your child when it comes to remembering things. Then, when they perform these tasks without being reminded, praise them for their efforts and encourage them to do more. Feedback is important; children must feel recognized and encouraged to change positive behavior. You can also use rewards and incentives to stimulate and promote positive behavioral change. For example, instead of telling your child their mistakes every time they act against the rules, try prompting them, "Do you remember what we discussed as a consequence if you continued to leave your toys lying around?" Instead of you doing all the talking, interact with them by asking questions allowing them to reflect on previous discussions you have had. This keeps an open conversation between you and your child.

You can also say, "You were kind to our visitors today; would you like to choose dessert tonight?" However, ensure that you refrain from repeating the same incentives. It might lose value over time, and they might become bored.

Avoid Restrictions

Do not restrict your child from physical movements and activities. Using this consequence method for your child's misbehavior has more negative impacts than positive ones. For example, if your child gets overly excited and runs around the house, causing a mess and being loud, you may feel frustrated and send them to their room so you can get a break.

The immediate results of this might seem favorable since you would have nothing to worry about for the next 30 minutes and save them from getting hurt. However, it would be best if you considered the long-term effect of such a punishment. Children with ADHD need lots of physical movement and exercise to exert focus. Allow them to be restless, as this helps them work more productively; they could lean against a table or lie down on their chest or back as long as it allows them to focus on the task. You might notice that your child likes to hold onto a fidget toy like a ball that helps them maintain focus for long periods when performing tasks. This is common amongst children with ADHD as it aids the process of maintaining attention.

Create a Schedule and Practice Routine

Children with ADHD need structure, and a schedule can help to support that. Reduce your child's workload and ensure the tasks are broken down according to your child's age and ability. On the other hand, do not overload them with work. There should be breaks between each daily task; it is important to help them understand the essence of structure and how it is beneficial to perform tasks.

They should know what tasks they have to carry out, how long each task will take, and how to check off the tasks that have been completed. To make this fun for your child, you can draw a chart with colorful pictures that lists the tasks and explains how to perform them in clear and simple terms. You can set a timer to ensure they stick to the stipulated time frame for each task. This keeps your child engaged and helps them to be responsible and effective around the house without giving them room for procrastination.

Remember that positive comments and accolades strengthen your child's resolve and attitude toward work. When you pay more attention to positive behaviors than negative ones, you stand a better chance of promoting behavioral changes. Constantly nagging or highlighting your child's negative behaviors can make you come off as an overbearing parent and unintentionally damage their self-esteem. To avoid that, apply a reward system that includes giving them tokens or stickers when they do a good job within the right timeframe or for following through on simple instructions. If your child is older, consider taking them to lunch or stopping at their favorite smoothie shop. Be sure to tell your child why you want to treat them, that you appreciate their behavior (be specific), and encourage them to keep up the good work.

Forgiveness

Martin Luther King once said, "We must strive to build and sustain the capacity to forgive. He who falls short of the power to forgive lacks the power to love."

Parenting is a challenging task, especially if you have a short fuse. In the heat of the moment, when your frustration and stress levels peak, your temper flares, and you impulsively make hurtful statements fueled by anger during family interactions or directly to your child. Young children and teenagers test limits; unsurprisingly, you would have difficulty managing intense feelings. However, resentment may trickle in over time.

Practicing forgiveness with your family shows how intentional you are about letting go of blame and thoughts of revenge towards those who have hurt your feelings, whether inadvertently or on purpose. Forgiveness doesn't imply that you overlook their wrongdoings or condone misbehavior; it simply means that you rid yourself of the heartache that comes with holding onto grudges and other ill feelings.

To forgive is to be compassionate and show love and mercy because, deep down inside, it is the most effective means of responding to crises in your relationship with your child and other people. Forgiveness also shapes your thoughts about people with ADHD by helping you understand the many environmental, emotional, and social factors influencing their behavior. With forgiveness, you understand in-depth that your responses and reactions can be controlled.

For example, when your child litters the house with his dirty socks, frightens the cat, or breaks your favorite photo frame because he was being hyperactive, practicing forgiveness in your mind towards yourself and your child will help you maintain control of your emotional outbursts and responses to the situation. True, it doesn't diminish or invalidate the fact that you were annoyed and disappointed in your child's actions; however, you chose to be more understanding, kind, and lenient because you know your child struggles with ADHD, and none of those actions are influenced by utter bad behavior.

In place of an angry reaction and emotional overload, forgiveness teaches you to be more logical in the process of disciplining your child. Other times, it just teaches you to let go.

It is easy for people to say you should always show compassion towards children and others without addressing how their actions initially made you feel. However, holding your head up, suppressing your negative emotions, and showing compassion is hard. It is even harder in the heat of the moment when your child has made you feel terrible; feeling immediate empathy is nearly unachievable.

Frequently, you might find yourself directing the anger elsewhere by behaving passive-aggressively towards other people in your life. You are not perfect, and no one should ever expect perfection when dealing with your emotions and restraining yourself from escalating the situation. You are not a miracle worker, either. Emotions are elastic—there are limits to how far they stretch. It takes willpower to create an open mind, practice forgiveness, and maintain consistency, even when difficult. The following tips can serve as guide-lines in the process of learning to accept yourself and forgive others, especially your children:

- Reduce the expectations you have of yourself concerning parenting skills.
- Instead of constantly berating yourself when your parenting measures fail to yield desired results, practice acceptance.
- Pay extra attention to your current resources and how you manage them rather than the resources you are still missing.
- It is okay to make mistakes; acknowledge them and strive to improve next time.
- Don't self-loathe or blame yourself.

- Start small. That is, forgive yourself for little things like snapping at your child because you are running late for getting them to school and situations where they do not perform tasks within the stipulated time frame you gave them.
- When faced with a thought-provoking situation, acknowledge it and brainstorm likely solutions.
- Don't strive to be a perfectionist.
- Forgiveness is a never-ending practice; free yourself of resentment and embrace your capacity for happiness, compassion, empathy, and contentment.
- Perform a loving-kindness meditation routine.
- Adaptability and understanding are key for ourselves and our children with ADHD. Often we remember the things that do not go right. But, we also need to take stock of what does. Try to remind yourself of the good each day. If it helps, keep a notebook, even if it is just for a few weeks, to get you into the habit of recalling something good from each day. Finding the positive instead of the negative is also good for our mental health. One thing I try to do every day is to ensure that my child's day doesn't start on a negative note. Maybe we are running behind, maybe they are being loud, or maybe

they didn't get their teeth brushed. I have made choices that I acknowledge which tasks did not get completed or have delayed us, but then ask how we get back on course tomorrow. I do not yell about the issue. It is unfair to your child to explode or yell at them and then send them off to school and expect them to be able to focus. Tell them you love them, have a great day, and can't wait to see them later.

SUPPORT FOR YOUR CHILD WITH ADHD

The most promising child with ADHD has a support system that is intentional and dedicated to shaping their life for a better future. Every child needs to feel supported and, most importantly, made to feel that they'll always find a safety net in their parents. You can only successfully achieve this as a parent when you fully understand what ADHD is and how you can be supportive. Unlocking the right ADHD coaching method for your child might be the key to establishing a healthy family life and mending your relationship with your child.

Many things can become difficult for a child with ADHD, and you need to recognize them. For example, many adults agree that nothing compares to getting a full night of sound sleep after an activity-filled day—

you desperately yearn to lay in the comfort of your bed and relax your tense muscles in preparation for the next day. The same applies to children, especially those with ADHD who have experienced peak activity levels all day. Unfortunately, they usually have difficulty getting a good night's sleep, which harms their health.

Every child should get a certain amount of sleep according to their age. In the absence of sufficient sleep, your child's health might suffer a decline. In addition, children with ADHD who have difficulty getting enough sleep tend to become less attentive in school and at home. The lack of attentiveness can, in turn, worsen their capabilities in school, during homework, while regulating emotions, and while socializing amongst their peers. As a parent, you might create a schedule encouraging your child to turn in early at night. If the child has been diagnosed with ADHD, however, this might be easier said than done because they tend to be over-stimulated most of the time and may have difficulty staying in bed for too long.

Other important aspects of their lives also require a solid support system. Developing and maintaining healthy eating and sleeping habits, helping them function appropriately in the home and social settings, setting expectations, and enacting positive parenting styles represent core approaches that can help a child with ADHD navigate life easier and become better versions of themselves. Remember that you do not have to be the perfect parent in showing support to your child. All you need to do is find the right balance between offering support and attention. Emotional regulation results from having a schedule, maintaining healthy eating and sleeping habits, and having strong parent modeling.

The following are actionable steps for supporting your child at home:

- Ensure that your child gets positive attention as often as possible. They should never feel neglected or different from their siblings and peers.
- Keep your child away from the TV before bedtime. There can be much overstimulation from watching a late-night animation or movie.
- Instead of seeing a movie before bedtime, try other, less stimulating activities like doing a quick puzzle or reading a bedtime story. This would also be a good time to teach your child about gratitude.
- Add a new healthy food to the meal plan every week. Your child should eat a balanced diet and drink lots of water. You might even get your

child to help you choose between a few food options to reward good behavior.

- Encourage exercise. This is an integral aspect of supporting your child through ADHD, as exercise promotes a happy vibe and, at the same time, keeps them healthy. It doesn't have to be strenuous—even walking can do the trick!
- Take parent coaching classes for parents of children with ADHD to help for a smoother parenting process with your child. Family therapy is also effective and essential to your child's growth.
- Don't yell at your children. Set clear expectations in the most simplified way possible and emphasize the consequences. Yelling at every mistake can make your child feel that they can never do anything right, and you are modeling that you cannot regulate your emotions, so why should they listen to you.

4

BUILD THEM UP!

The stepping stone to a better and progressive parenting style for children who have ADHD is understanding what the disorder entails and moving on to identify effective and ineffective measures for managing it. Building up children right from their infant years into other developmental stages requires a good understanding of the positive and the negative. Children are mentally fragile and have impressionable minds, so the wrong measures can jeopardize their healthy growth. You do not want to be in the position where you make a statement in a fit of anger that stays ingrained in your child's memory and affects their sense of self. You can recognize that you are not a perfect parent, but it is essential also to remember what tools create good parenting for children with this diagnosis and what to avoid. Children with ADHD who have moments of explosive behavior will require even more care to build them up so that you can ensure that they can have a positive and happy life. They likely hate how they feel when experiencing the behavior, but they need your help to deal with it, both when they are with you and in situations when you aren't there, such as at school or with friends. Your child's ADHD is something they will have to deal with their entire life; therefore, finding the right coping methods for them early on can pave the way for their future. Finding the right methods may also require trial and error, as what works for one child with ADHD will not necessarily be the same for another child, even if they have the same ADHD symptoms.

POSITIVE REINFORCEMENT

Parenting styles differ from family to family. The family structure and environmental and social factors determine how the "average" child turns out in the future. For example, children raised by authoritarian parents experience growth under strict rules and high expectations that control rather than nurture them. On the other hand, positive reinforcement represents an alternative parenting style. In this case, you are encouraged to apply a reward system when your child does what you taught them.

For example, imagine you are walking with your child at the park, and they mistakenly bump into a stranger because they were not looking, and then say, "oh, I'm sorry." This may seem new and unexpected to you because you have constantly reminded them of being polite to people but have not witnessed them put it into action. Following this new development in your child, reinforce their positive behavior by, for example, getting them a popsicle or extending their playtime. Regardless of the reward, tell them that you witnessed this behavior and you are proud of them. Your child understands that their reward results from their polite behavior earlier at the park; therefore, they are encouraged to do it again.

This parenting style encourages children to be respectful and well-behaved without using violent discipline, threats, physical and emotional abuse, humiliation, shame, or punishment at the slightest provocation. You should adopt the positive reinforcement parenting method with your child for several reasons. First, even if this concept is new, it can still be effective. The disciplinary methods you grew up with or have seen from other parents don't have to be the ones you use. Keeping an open mind when parenting

your child with ADHD is important, and positive reinforcement can work. Managing children with ADHD
when school is in session can feel like a lot, but imagine
that it is summer break, and you must take full responsibility when their symptoms peak. What do you do
then? How do you enforce an effective positive reinforcement style without worrying that your child might
slip into bad behavior again and feeling the toll it takes
on your well-being? Some tips include:

- Pay extra attention to your child's environment
  and plan accordingly. For example, when your
  toddler is hungry, they are likely to throw a fit,
  so you can tell they need food. Also, when
  children are tired or overwhelmed, they tend to
  exhibit extreme behavioral patterns that ADHD
  influences. It would be best if you were
  prepared for moments like this by providing
  food for your child minutes before they are due
  for the meal, ensuring that their needs are met
  and preventing any type of explosive reaction.
- Do not hold back when giving your child well-
  deserved accolades for performing a task or
  showing good morals. Be sure to highlight the
  good quality that has earned them praise
  specifically. If they put their dishes in the
  dishwasher after using them, tell them, "I see

you put your dishes in the dishwasher. I appreciate that. Thank you." Tell them clearly and simply what they have done right and why you are pleased with it. When you notice your child has prevented themselves from having an explosive moment, this is the time to recognize that. "Hey, I want to say thank you for not getting upset when your friend wasn't nice to you today. You let her know you were upset but did not yell or lose control. You did a good job."

- Become familiar with positive reinforcement phrases like "You have done a good job," "Well done," "Thank you," "This is wonderful," etc. Remember that over-using these terms can make your child too familiar with them and, thus, may decrease their value. Therefore, develop new phrases from time to time to keep your child's interest.

- Avoid instilling confusion in your child as to what you expect of them. Be clear with your expectations so they can fully understand what you require of them and where you draw the line. For example, if you frown on watching television during mealtime but overlook the action when your child flouts the rule once, you might send mixed signals about what you deem acceptable.

- Avoid only giving verbal cues to reinforce positive behavior in your children; use visual cues that can serve as directions to help them remain focused on the tasks you have assigned. With consistent practice, your child will understand certain visual cues and what they mean while fulfilling obligations.

TRIGGERING PHRASES TO AVOID

Every parent has the well-being of their children at heart; you always want to be positive around them and say reassuring and encouraging things. However, children with ADHD can test your limits so much that you might get out of line and make insensitive statements that could damage your child's mental and emotional growth. Some of these phrases include:

- "Don't blame your ADHD. It's not an excuse." Truly, this diagnosis is not an excuse for lagging in certain aspects of life. However, people with this disorder, especially children, have no control over it. They struggle mentally and emotionally. They often need to be efficient in assigned tasks and complete them on time. They want to be able to pay unflinching attention and focus but cannot do so successfully because the disorder creates roadblocks. ADHD affects the ability to exert self-control, and managing hyperactive and overwhelming emotions can be just as strenuous. None of these insufficiencies is their fault. It would be insensitive to rub it squarely in their face that they are to blame for being unable to function adequately like other children.

Instead of making this statement, you can replace it with, "I understand you have ADHD, and that makes things more difficult for you. I still need you to be accountable, so how can I help?" and "What would you have done differently if given a chance to make changes?"

- "Everyone can get distracted sometimes, and you aren't any different." The reality of this statement is that while everyone can experience distraction occasionally, it is not the same with children with ADHD. They are easily distracted all the time! This statement might not necessarily imply that you are trying to make your child feel bad about their disorder, and perhaps you just do not want them ever to feel alone and different; however, you are not facing the facts. You will be giving your child a false sense of relief. Children with this diagnosis tend to get easily distracted—with friends, in school, amongst family members, and in society.

They are not like other children, which is okay; there is no stigma. Instead of making this statement, tell them that everyone in the universe has situations they struggle with, and theirs is not uncommon. Assure them that they are unique but not alone.

- "You can focus on your video games, so maybe try focusing harder on other things. It shouldn't be that hard." Children with predominantly inattentive symptoms tend to only focus on things that interest them or come with a sense of urgency. With other tasks, they might need help to apply the same focus level successfully. This is how their brain functions; they have no control over it. Telling your child that they should focus on work the same way they focus on things they find fun is like saying they had a choice but have refused to do so.
- It also means you have difficulty believing your child has a problem focusing on things and that they may be selective about tasks as an avenue

to be lazy. Instead of making this horrifying statement, say, "I understand doing this work can be difficult for you. How can we break the tasks down, so they are more manageable? We will build breaks into the tasks as well."

- "You don't need to tell anyone you have ADHD. They don't need to know." You might be your child's direct caregiver, but you are not the only one leaving an imprint on your child. They have friends, schoolteachers, sports coaches, and so on that will be a part of their life whether you like it or not. How do you expect your child to get other people's support and guidance if they are private about disclosing their ADHD? If you encourage your child to keep their mouth sealed about their disorder, you will inadvertently enable others to criticize and judge them harshly. Here's another hurtful instance. Say you have a full-spirited child who is overly playful at a particular moment. You may be urged to ask if they have taken their medications to quell their hyperactive behavior. This can feel awful to a child because they were probably engaging in harmless fun, and how awful they might feel if they truly did take their meds and their parents criticized their normal childish behavior.

Making this statement does not in any way protect your child. Instead, you enable them to become vulnerable to social isolation and neglect. Having this disorder isn't something you should be ashamed of. Instead, creating awareness that they have ADHD can help people understand them better and work around it. Treating your child respectfully and coming to terms with their diagnosis is necessary when dealing with it. Especially if your child exhibits explosive behavior or acts inappropriately because of their ADHD, you may feel embarrassed about it. This could cause you to react incorrectly, especially if you are in public and want to take some of the focus away from you. However, your child is likely to recall your reactions. Therefore, to help your child, you must remember how hurtful the triggering words and actions are.

MANAGING YOUR REACTIONS

Words and phrases like "stupid," "lazy," "you should be ashamed of yourself," and "I do not care" should be erased from your vocabulary when you are dealing with your children. They can trigger self-esteem issues in your children because your words emphasize their inadequacies and incompetence. For example, imagine that your child struggles to get their schoolwork done and lags academically, so you blurt out of annoyance and frustration, "I don't understand why this is so hard for you. It's easy." Your child recoils in shame as your words echo in their head repeatedly, and the criticism hits home. They might never recover from that; at every juncture where they need to improve and overcome inattention or compulsivity, your words keep reminding them of how they are incapable of doing anything successfully. This new thought process will cripple their chances of evolving even before they have begun.

No child deserves to constantly hear criticisms from their parents about how they cannot behave like other children or how they have so much to put up with — parents are the models they revere and look up to for guidance and support. Therefore, you must learn to manage your emotions when on the verge of an outburst. Instead of focusing on their wrongdoings and always paying extra attention to their flaws, focus on the positive. For example, if your child does the dishes for the first time, focus on the newly developed sense of duty and accomplishment, and praise them for it instead of emphasizing how they didn't load the dishwasher efficiently or didn't get the dishes clean enough. Praise and teach.

Sometimes, as humans, it can be exhausting to constantly hear someone nag and complain about everything we do wrong. This can be overwhelming for children with ADHD because every feeling is heightened for them. A simple hug and a "thank you" or "you have done well; I am proud of you" is all it takes to encourage your child to do better and keep progressing. Children with ADHD are already known to be more disorganized than other children, but they are exceptional at remembering important details about subjects that excite them. As a parent, you should focus more on these strengths and find measures to help them stimulate and strengthen the things they do better.

Employ the use of humor to ease the intensity coursing through your child's veins. Making a joke can unknot your child when they are sad; it brightens their mood and helps them to feel better about negative or difficult situations. Assign tasks like writing a simple list of things that make them happy or things they want to learn about to let them explore their hobbies and other subjects that excite and stimulate their interests. They are more efficient when given tasks that allow them to discuss and express their feelings about a favorite topic. Most importantly, learn to forgive yourself.

Your child can achieve healthy growth and a fun family lifestyle. However, you are an experienced adult, and it is up to you to find strategies that help build up your relationship successfully. Offer your child immeasurable love and affection, and do not hesitate to apologize when you handle situations poorly. Whether a child with ADHD becomes a functional adult lies mostly in their caregiver's hands. Do not cause lifelong consequences through the poor management of your emotions.

5

SHOWING THE WAY

Empathy plays a significant role in any human interaction or relationship. Every person—young and old—wants to feel heard, loved, and understood. Children with ADHD in all spheres of their lives should be empathized with just as much as they need to be capable of showing empathy. This exchange can only be made possible if you have a child who understands what empathy entails and how it can greatly impact their lives and others. The question is, what does it mean to be empathetic?

EMPATHY

Empathy is understanding someone else's feelings, including their perspective. Instead of responding, you are listening to understand other people's perceptions and imagine their feelings about the situation. For example, say your teenage daughter returns from school one day and complains to you about an argument with her best friend. Based on her story, you can already tell that your daughter is to blame for the fight. So instead of faulting her, you make statements like, "I bet that made you feel sad and disappointed." With empathy, you can experience your child's mental and emotional distress and become sensitive to it, so it is easy to console them with the right words.

What every child and adult needs during an overwhelming emotional experience is a supportive, understanding, and empathetic listener. When these traits are absent, you are most likely dealing with a narcissistic child or adult. Therefore, encouraging empathy in children with ADHD is important for a healthy family relationship and for how they interact with friends and other people.

IS YOUR ADHD CHILD UNSYMPATHETIC?

Has your child shown behavioral patterns suggesting difficulty identifying other people's feelings? Or perhaps they disregard others' feelings easily and focus too much on themselves? Children with ADHD tend to act impulsively, be hyperactive, lose interest in things, and find it difficult to concentrate for long. All of these ADHD symptoms can influence their ability to empathize. How can anyone listen attentively when it is hard to maintain focus? Or how can anyone imagine and internalize another's pain and perspective when easily distracted and impulsive? Exactly—it is going to be a struggle.

Sometimes, it is not that your child is unsympathetic. Instead, they are unaware of the demeanor they are expected to assume when other people are having a bad time. Hence, they are indifferent and unsympathetic toward people. If this nature persists in your child until adulthood, they may have difficulty maintaining close relationships with friends, and having a best friend would only be a fantasy. Likewise, being cordial with siblings and parents will also be difficult, as the absence of empathy drives a wedge through families.

This does not necessarily have to be the case. Your child can develop a strong sense of empathy. Being an empathetic child is a strength. It is beneficial to them, to you as their parent, to their siblings, and to the society they become a part of.

The following tips can help your child embrace empathy and live a better life:

- Demonstrate empathy toward others. Teaching empathy has much more to do with demonstrating than merely instructing. Children tend to pick up important details when acceptable behavioral patterns are modeled.
- Express compassion, kindness, and love towards your children and other people when your children are present. They'll learn quickly.
- Do not suppress your emotions with your child. Teach them to positively express their feelings verbally and respond to them how you hope they would respond if they were in your position. If they have difficulty expressing their emotions verbally, there are other tools you can use, such as pictograms or asking them to draw a picture to attempt to explain their emotions.
- Do not ignore or belittle their emotions. Every little feeling and expression should count.
- Celebrate your child's successes, no matter how small. Do not downplay their efforts.
- Teach your child to identify feelings. For example, what gives sad people away? What kind

of facial expressions do they make? How can
your child become sensitive around them and
empathize? Teach them the negative impressions
they leave when unaware of how their actions
affect others. That is, create awareness.

- Teach them to bounce back from adversities
  and become stronger. Resilience helps to build
  empathy in children; therefore, they need to
  learn how to be good problem-solvers. This
  does not mean ignoring their feelings just to
  move past them. Instead, they need to be taught
  how to recognize their feelings and manage and
  resolve them.
- Explain to your child that there are different
  kinds of people in the world with varying belief
  systems, cultures, lifestyles, and faiths. Teach
  them that everyone is unique in their way and
  that no one should be segregated. Every
  individual deserves love, compassion, and
  empathy.
- Be patient. It is going to be more than a one-
  day job. You will have to exercise lots of
  patience to establish and sustain empathy in
  your child. Work together as a family.
- It is okay to seek help when you feel lost about
  what to do and how to handle your child with

ADHD. Seek professional help or join support groups.

STAYING POSITIVE

It is becoming increasingly difficult for the average person to maintain a positive outlook on life. Everyone has hurdles they need to overcome on an almost daily basis. So many factors can test your resolve, and it is only human to respond accordingly. Now, imagine what that feels like for people—especially children—with ADHD. As a parent, if you also have ADHD, praise you as you understand their struggles. You have to manage a home and care for children who likely have the disorder and can get out of hand. You are also on the verge of losing it, yet you must maintain positivity, peace, and order around the house. That's a god-level ability.

There are lots of methods to help you maintain positivity in the house and also simplify its impact on you as a parent:

- Put your well-being at the top of your list of priorities. An African proverb says it takes a fed, refreshed horse to help humans travel farther. The horse will only make it very far if it is sufficiently fed and refreshed. In a metaphorical sense, you are your child's horse, saddled with the responsibility to love and care for them and to see them through each stage of development and growth—with or without ADHD. Regardless of these overwhelming tasks, it would be best to learn ways to control your temper and withhold negative outbursts that could negatively influence your child. Schedule thirty minutes or an hour of your day for personal time and take a break to be alone. Meditate often and tap into nature to help you feel refreshed and enable a positive mindset.

- Work together as a family. Keeping peace and order in the home should be more than your responsibility; it can become overwhelming over time. Instead, break down tasks and split them up amongst your children and partner. Let your children clean their rooms and pick up their toys and dirty laundry so you can create time to organize your workspace. This way, it is manageable. Your child's age should be considered, as you do not want to overwhelm them either. Set a daily schedule for what tasks should be completed and when. You can make this fun by turning it into a family game with a reward. For example, the fastest person to complete a task in a neat and organized manner could win a prize.

- Encourage family events that strengthen bonds. Bonding is an essential factor that influences healthy growth in families and helps to enhance positivity. For example, you can introduce a family bonding weekly event such as going on a nature walk, growing a garden together, or playing an interactive game where there is plenty to keep a child with ADHD focused. Also, children with ADHD may be able to focus for hours when it comes to their passions. There may be bonding activities that can be built around those pastimes that the whole family will like. For children with ADHD, family-sharing opportunities help them express themselves positively and mentally note the tasks they must commit to the following week.

- For some activities, using a timer will also let a child with ADHD know how long the activity will take. More frequent activities with shorter times attached to them can be beneficial for children who lose focus easily.

- Have fun. In everything you do as a family, have fun. Young children naturally radiate energy, and children with ADHD are over the top. You should help them channel these energy surges into activities that benefit them. Make sure you have fun things to look forward to as a family rather than repetitive daily tasks and chores. Put something new and fun on the calendar for you and your children. These events are the sparks your family needs to keep positivity stirring in the air.

FORGIVE IGNORANCE

People can be illogical, judgmental, unreasonable, and ignorant of certain things. However, it would help if you forgave them when they hurt you as long as you understand that your ability to exercise forgiveness liberates and brings you peace to move on with life. Forgiveness does not imply that you excuse the emotional hurt from being misjudged. It simply shows that you are one step ahead. With ADHD, your child is bound to face certain challenges, like having difficulty making friends and sustaining friendships. Regardless, children must be amongst their peers and engage in social activities. This is why you need to take extra measures to ensure your child learns to explain their disorder to their friends. Moreover, with people older than they are, make it your duty to intercede on their behalf.

Say you are at a store with your child, and they ask for a toy. After you refuse this request, your child goes into a full-on meltdown and eventually even starts to grab things off the shelves and throw them. Now you have other parents staring at you and possibly judging you. They do not understand what your child is going through, and their judgment should not affect your parenting style. Even in public, you should be able to come down to your child's level and work with them to calm their nerves, just as you would at home.

Most times, people tend to judge what they do not understand properly. Therefore, it is important that the people around your child—including family, friends, and teachers—are aware of their disorder; make sure to be open about the diagnosis. This makes it easier for people to understand why your child might be slightly different from other children and to show empathy toward them.

There are ways you can enlighten friends, family, and acquaintances who are a part of your child's life about what ADHD is and how it influences certain behavioral patterns in your child. Remember that enlightenment might not necessarily guarantee your child will be understood; some people might never be able to grasp the concept of ADHD. They might even begin to question certain things and hurt your feelings or your child's; this is ignorance. You must learn to forgive such people and continue enlightening them when you can. Some tips for doing so include:

- Make a script. Every human being has different and varying confidence levels regarding verbal expression, especially with delicate matters. If you think you might have difficulty explaining ADHD correctly to people without omitting important details, you should write a script for how you want the conversation to play out. Practice and perfect the sentences to help you build enough confidence for the conversation.
- Be positive when relaying information. In the process of enlightening people, you should avoid sounding overly assertive. Instead, you should embody positivity and communicate your gratitude for the person's presence in your child's life and for their role. This way, you have established a good foundation for them to empathize with your child when you share information about their disorder.
- Explain your child's diagnosis as specifically as you can. Be certain about your child's predominant symptoms and how they compare to neurotypical children, and state the differences. Some children with ADHD

undergo behavioral treatments or medications, while others might have a combination. Therefore, whatever treatment has been administered by the pediatrician or specialist for your child's disorder, ensure that you enlighten others properly. If you have goals to help your child lead a much more fulfilling life, you can also share those. Some friends and family might be interested in helping you actualize some of these goals. Please encourage them to ask questions and provide substantial answers to them. This way, you can learn what issues your loved ones have no idea about and help them to understand.

- Show support to your child's teachers. Since your child spends most of their day within the four walls of the school and the remaining hours of the day in the house, you can be sure their teachers are just as overwhelmed by their hyperactivity as you are. Not every teacher understands the influences and impact of ADHD on children. Your child might become difficult to manage. Therefore, when your child's teacher brings to your knowledge how hard it is to keep your child reined, be ready to partner with them. Ensure that the line of communication is always open and that you are always ready to share strategies for alleviating their concern and managing your child's behavior in school.

- Maintain some distance from those who are unsupportive. Truly, to forgive is divine. Sometimes you are better off not being in contact with people who are hell-bent on failing to see the bright side of the situation. Some family members and friends may never get on board with your child's ADHD diagnosis; they may even make derogatory statements to hurt your and your child's feelings. Understand that it is important to forgive them to avoid the emotional burden, but do not keep them in close contact. ADHD is not the end of your child's life; they can thrive like every other neurotypical child. You do not need to be in contact with unsupportive people.

Showing your child ways to react appropriately in situations is the best method that you can use to help them to succeed in life. When you show them how to interact with people, it can help them understand appropriate behaviors. For some children with ADHD, especially if they have explosive behavior issues, it can require additional work and conversations to help them understand that the way they sometimes react isn't their fault. But, even when it is not their fault, it doesn't mean they can't learn coping methods to help improve things in the future. There are many different avenues that you can take to show your children the best ways to react to situations. In addition to the explanations above, talking out issues as well as role-playing scenarios can also be effective.

6

ADHD ADVOCACY

Children will thrive under most circumstances. However, if they are struggling, chances are there is an obstacle hindering their success despite their efforts. These obstacles must be addressed, and you can do so by advocating for your child's needs. In addition, advocacy creates greater awareness, which can help your child and others who are just as easily misunderstood due to their disorder. As ADHD presents differently in each individual and cannot be diagnosed with a simple test, it can be more trying to advocate effectively. It can be even more complicated if the child has behavioral and emotional issues. With these issues, it can be more challenging to pinpoint the underlying causes and deal with them. Since you cannot always be with your child, you need to advocate for them so that other adults can support them when they cannot independently regulate their emotions and behaviors.

ADVOCATING FOR YOUR CHILD WITH ADHD

As a parent, you can imagine your child's struggle when they must work twice as hard to succeed compared to neurotypical children. Often, even when given the same learning opportunities, children with ADHD have greater difficulty achieving the same level of success as other children. This produces a lot of mental and physical stress on children with ADHD, and older children may even suffer from occasional emotional breakdowns. Other times, they can be subjected to bullying. People who are ignorant of the disorder's impact call them clumsy, badly behaved, annoying, lousy, and other negative terms. As a result, children may carry the stigma on for most of their lives and never recover. Advocacy can help address such ignorance and eradicate the chances of lifelong implications for your child.

Advocating for your child with ADHD should be done in the home, school, doctor's office, and community. These are places your child's life revolves around and where they will come into contact with people from all walks of life with different perspectives on ADHD and other disorders.

HOW TO ADVOCATE EFFECTIVELY

Naturally, you want to give your child the best home, school, and community support. You may worry that you can only do your best within the confines of the home and a little when it comes to advocating in the community. School, however, might seem out of your jurisdiction, as teachers are equipped to do their jobs. There is a lot you can do as an effective advocate in every aspect of your child's life. The following are some measures to take into consideration during the process:

- Keep an open line of communication with your child. The effectiveness of healthy communication cannot be overstated. Children tend to excel academically, function better amongst their peers, and make healthier choices when they have a warm and healthy relationship with their parents. Direct ice-breaking questions like, "what part of school do you enjoy the most?" "What is your favorite thing to do?" and "What is your least favorite subject in school?" should be asked regularly if you aim to help your child overcome primary school challenges.
- Identify how your child's behaviors at home and in school are different. Your child spends

up to six hours in school, and chances are the teacher knows how they function in this setting. Consistently, but not too frequently, contact the teacher for information and updates on your child's strengths and weaknesses. Get comfortable asking their teacher how well they function, deal with being organized, and stay focused on their assigned tasks. Inquire about their social behavior: Do they get along well with other children? Are there situations of violence? Etc. This information will help you become an effective advocate for your child.

- Get support for your child as soon as you can. Be sure to take action on significant matters that concern your child before the school organizes a parent-teacher conference. Request a comprehensive evaluation of your child's academic, cognitive, social, and emotional functioning in the school. The teacher should give a personal perspective on your child's progress over time, as federal law requires special education services for children with ADHD and other disorders. This provides them with the same learning opportunities as their peers to fulfill their potential; the school is expected to take measures to ensure the implementation of this requirement.

- Meet the people who evaluate your child. Most schools provide a written evaluation of a child; your child's school should not be any different. Those who will evaluate your child must make decisions in that regard. The results should be discussed so you can decipher whether the basic educational objectives are being met. Request an independent one if you realize they are not being met or that certain things need to be changed or adjusted during the evaluation.
- Be sensitive to your child's moods. Being diagnosed with ADHD as a child is very challenging. Children rarely have it easy in any aspect of their lives. A large number of these children also have dyslexia and can potentially develop depression over time when they become adults. Therefore, one of the best ways to support your child is to be sensitive to their moods and emotions. Parental instincts should be trusted when concerned about your children's well-being. Do not brush aside the small voice that points out something different about your child's behavior. You can confidently say you know your child well enough because you have spent years raising them and understanding their behavioral patterns. So, when you pay extra attention to

those moments when their moods falter due to a change in their environment, issues at school with a decline in grades, or disagreement with friends, you will know how to empathize and take action to help them become better.

- Become familiar with the Individual Education Plan (IEP). In order to effectively advocate for your child with ADHD, you must understand what the IEP process entails and how it can benefit them. The education plan is created by the parents, teachers, and experts on special education, amongst others. It serves the purpose of considering a child's specific needs and outlining curricula with goals that aid the child's success academically. With the plan, you can easily monitor your child's progress and assess whether your child is meeting the required practical goals and how much support you can give to simplify things.

TIPS

Most children with ADHD are constantly subjected to stigma in school environments and the community. Even though they are problematic and unfair, these stigmas still exist, and children can become victims. People tend to make judgments and say unfair things, whether to your child's face or behind your back, without any consideration for conversations with you that could enlighten them further. Research has shown that there are parents who prevent their children from associating with children who exhibit hyperactivity and impulsiveness because they find the behaviors non-conforming and do not want their children influenced negatively. These stigmas do the community a great disservice, and your child might be subjected to them at some point.

The following are practical tips that can help to prevent or lessen the implications of unfair treatment and stigmas on your child:

- Be educated on the benefits of reducing stigma. Knowledge is power. You need to gain basic knowledge to know how to impact something positively. Taking on a big role, such as being an advocate for ADHD, requires a vast knowledge base to help your child and reduce stigmas in the important areas of any child's life. Most parents of children with ADHD often complain and become overwhelmed by the intensity of their child's behavior and how they can be very difficult to manage around the house. You can easily tell from how upset they are that they have little knowledge of how ADHD works.

Until they can transcend that ignorance, they might never be able to understand, let alone advocate for ADHD. Sometimes, having significant knowledge is all it takes to effect the big change you want in your child's life.

- Pursue behavioral parent training. Being a parent to children with ADHD already guarantees that you are saddled with great responsibility, including caring for the child and advocating for their disorder. One of the most effective ways to handle children with ADHD and ensure improvement is through behavioral management techniques. It is also important for teachers who are academically responsible for children within that age range to provide behavior management techniques to help improve the lives of children with ADHD.

- Participate in the school system. The baseline for this tip is to become acquainted with the basic knowledge of what ADHD entails more than anyone else because you have to care for a child with ADHD. It is strongly recommended that you consider being a volunteer in your child's classroom, even if it is just once or twice a month. Doing so will help you understand what the teacher expects of the children and how you can reinforce the same expectations in the home. This way, you can easily strike a balance in the behavioral consistency of your child in school and at home.

- Seek help from your community. It always helps to know what professionals or organizations you can contact in the community for advice and learn the rights and policies surrounding advocacy. Every school, workplace, and community has a distinctive language for how things operate; if you need help understanding the language, you might have difficulty being an advocate. In every community you hope to advocate, ensure you know "who is who" and "what is what."

- Be observant and learn to convey expectations. Often, people's actions will not align with your expectations if you do not communicate them. If your child's school is not enlightened on ADHD or what you expect of them concerning your child, potential challenges could arise. See your child's teachers as members of your advocacy team, and work with them for your child's progress and improvement—do not work against them. Take your time observing how your child functions in the school environment to serve as a pointer to how they can be managed in the house and vice versa.

Your child, despite being young, is not always
innocent. Sometimes, children tend to cook up
lies against their teachers because they are not
allowed to have their way. You must observe
keenly without prejudice and convey your
expectations for every community in which you
advocate.

TEACHING YOUR CHILD SELF-ADVOCACY

Self-advocacy is a skill that every child with ADHD or
any other kind of disorder needs to learn. Your child
will mature as they grow and reach new developmental
stages. With maturity comes responsibility and, most
importantly, the need to advocate for themselves. Self-
advocacy increases children's potential for lifelong
success, and parents constantly underestimate its
importance. The fact that you now understand the
importance of helping your child self-advocate indicates that you are willing to help them hone it as a life
skill and learn the strategies they need to succeed in
every aspect of life, now and in the future.

The following are invaluable pointers to kick-start the process of helping your child develop self-advocacy skills:

- Begin at an early stage. Children are very sensitive; your child might constantly be reminded that they talk too much, ask too many questions, or are not well-behaved. The reactions they get from teachers and their peers might spark negative feelings, so you need to reassure them when they are still young and impressionable. Make them understand that teachers will always respect active learners and have no problem helping all students, irrespective of their learning styles.

- Instill self-awareness. Your child should have an in-depth understanding of their strengths and deficits. Encouraging self-awareness helps your child understand what is at stake and how to improve to lead a better lifestyle. Your child should never feel alone or alienated from their peers because they have no idea how to advocate for themselves. You should help them learn how to seek help positively. Reinforce that with the use of a polite and positive attitude and advocacy can yield favorable outcomes. For practical purposes, use role-playing to perform situations that may seem uncomfortable or impossible for your child to get past. This way, they can apply the same approach in real-life situations and overcome fear and insecurity.

- Stay positive. Positivity drives most of life's successes. Provide vivid examples of people with learning differences who have made it to the top through positive self-talk and the determination to prevail. Your child should understand that learning differences have nothing to do with their intelligence or capabilities.

- Build self-esteem. To guarantee successful self-advocacy, your child needs to be free of low self-esteem and, instead, radiate confidence. It is impossible to advocate for yourself when you do not feel best. Therefore, if you have caught your child doing something right or extraordinary, do not hesitate to praise the effort they put into completing it.

- Support critical thinking. It would be best if you always created avenues for your child to develop the act of thinking critically, especially in non-confrontational situations. Help your child to develop strengths and address weaknesses so that when faced with situations in which you are not there to advocate for them, they can confidently speak for themselves.

- Make plans for the future. It is one thing to help your child live through the present; it is another to help them prepare adequately for the future. Children are constantly experiencing growth and development in every aspect of life. With ADHD, they must be prepared for real-life situations like summer school, internships, college, applying for jobs, etc. Since they will most likely be away from your direct guidance, you must prepare them for the transition.

A WELCOME BREAK

"Only by giving are you able to receive more than you already have"

— *REV. JESSE JACKSON*

Let's take a break.

It feels good, doesn't it? Just a moment to take a breath without taking in any new information or having to handle a situation with the kids.

You probably don't get many of these moments... Not many parents of children with ADHD do. So it's important that you *do* give yourself a break – both in terms of how much you expect of yourself, and in the practical sense. Those advocacy tips in Chapter 6 are important... remember that advocating for your child is another way to show them that they are not alone in their diagnosis.

Take a moment, too, to acknowledge the extra work you're putting in to help your child and your own journey as a parent. You don't have a lot of time, but you're here now, with this book. Don't be hard on yourself if you can't read the whole thing. Your life is full, and you're doing everything you can.

Nonetheless, if you'd like to make this break last a moment longer, you have a glorious opportunity to help out other parents of children with ADHD.

<u>By leaving a review of this book on Amazon</u>, you'll help other parents who are looking for this guidance to find it quickly and easily.

No matter how much you've read, sharing how it has helped you and what information you've found here will signpost to other new readers with limited time and energy where they can find the help they're looking for. You're doing an amazing job. Thank you for helping me to make sure other parents know they are too.

If you are in the UK, please scan the QR code below to leave your review.

If you are in the US, please scan the QR code below to leave your review.

7

MANAGING ADHD AT HOME

Parenting on its own is a tedious task that demands patience and a great deal of sacrifice. Given how taxing parenting already is, raising a child with ADHD requires even more effort. The normal ways and routines you need to organize in the home are different and form unique routines. The degree of adjustments you must make to give your child a secure home environment depends on the type and severity of your child's symptoms. This means you must adopt different strategies or approaches to find what works the best and gives your child a quality living experience despite their symptoms.

Managing a child with ADHD in the home setting comes with a whole lot of changes. Understandably, there are several points at which your natural strength falters. In addition, the entire process can become more frustrating to cope with than you had anticipated when dealing with some of the behaviors which result from your child's ADHD, but rest assured, there are helpful approaches you can adopt to make life easier both for you and your child.

The first step starts with accepting and understanding your child's disorder. We talked about these in previous chapters, but going over some of the points raised earlier will offer keener insights on this particular topic, especially concerning how you, as a loving parent, can recognize the symptoms and behaviors in your child and better understand their actions and how to respond.

If their disorder was not diagnosed, most people might assume a child with ADHD is lazy, stubborn, and rebellious. However, suppose the child has explosive behaviors as part of their ADHD symptoms. In that case, other people's perceptions of them can be even worse as explosive behaviors result in meltdowns and outbursts at some of the most minor things. As a result, they may resort to lashing out harshly at the child or berating them emotionally. Such an ignorant approach would destroy the child's self-esteem and damage your relationship with them because they would withdraw and feel unsafe with you.

This is why it is necessary to recognize the child's ADHD and know that this influences their behavior and actions. With this knowledge, you can learn helpful ways to modify your home environment conducive to the child's growth and regulate your emotional responses to be more accommodating. So, understanding that this disorder and its accompanying symptoms make children act in ways that are hard for parents to manage will give you one less headache to fret over.

Your child with ADHD can still learn important life lessons and get the same education as other children their age. However, this means you must develop a different, better, kinder, and softer way of parenting the child. Your job as a parent now falls under providing an environment and structures that prevent the child from hurting themselves based on their impulsiveness and help them complete expected tasks successfully, have meaningful interactions, and build relationships with others.

THE IMPORTANCE OF STRUCTURE AND ROUTINE IN MANAGING ADHD AT HOME

We know that parents contribute a large percentage to the child's development in our society. If you are now parenting a child with ADHD, you will have to modify your behavior and learn to manage your child's behavior to foster their development. You will also need to adjust the home environment, enact certain routines and systems limiting your child's destructive behavior, and encourage your child to overcome self-doubt and develop confidence and self-esteem.

Children with ADHD generally have deficits in executive function. This means they do not possess the ability to think and plan, organize, control impulses, and complete tasks. Their attention span is low, and they are prone to rash and impulsive actions and hardly focus on tasks. Having to cope with these behavioral inconsistencies from your child as a parent is stressful and tiring. However, setting up an efficient structure in the form of consistent routines and house rules will help achieve two key things—reducing the stressful moments you have to endure and shaping the behavior of your child with ADHD. You and your child get the best out of this arrangement, and it also improves your relationship with them.

The many benefits of a structured environment for your child must be considered. First, knowing what to expect brings a sense of security and safety. This is what you get from establishing routines. It helps your child feel safe, and in that cocoon of safety, the child can now develop life skills, build healthy habits, and improve their interactions and relations with those around them.

Setting up a good routine offers safety and predictability in their daily life, teaches the child to manage time better, and gives them the confidence to perform their daily tasks effectively. This creates structure, helps them be more productive and disciplined, and develops good habits.

For you as a parent, routines would help reduce the stress you have had to deal with and alleviate the accompanying anxiety. As a result, you can find time for other enjoyable activities.

Below are some of the benefits routines can have for your child:

- Allows the child to develop positive habits: This can be traced to the fact that developing a habit takes practice and repetition; the more you practice something, the longer it stays with you and becomes part of you. So, providing your child with a routine will allow them to learn positive habits.
- Improves the ability to handle tasks: Many children can structure their chores, schedules, and activities, but such a seemingly easy feat is not the same for a child with ADHD. Handling

duties and activities becomes more complex because of how the disorder impairs their ability to be organized. With a set routine, you can guide your child through the activities they should carry out until they learn to perform them independently.

- Alleviates parents' stress and exhaustion: With a routine, the family becomes more organized and has time freed up for fun and enjoyable activities. This gives parents and children a healthy opportunity to bond, play, relax, or be creative.

- Inspires a sense of responsibility in children: A routine instills a sense of responsibility in children because they know what they need to do and when to do it. Knowing their duty, chore, or activity, they set off to do it. This can be incentivized with a reward system.

- Provides external control: The symptoms of ADHD lead to problems with self-control since the child is prone to impulsive behavior and cannot plan analytically or think ahead. Setting up a routine or structure will provide your child with a structured life and help them manage their symptoms successfully.

- Reduces conflicts: Another benefit of structures is that they help parents to regulate their emotional responses to the behavior of the child, lessen the arguments, anxiety, and family stress that would have ensued, and at the same time, improve the child's behavior.

- Creates a feeling of inclusion: When there is a structure in the home, and everyone is obligated to adhere to the routine, this will reduce the chances that your child will feel left out. Having uniformity from other family members makes the child with ADHD more willing and eager to participate in the structured arrangement.

- Establishes a blueprint for success: By establishing routines, positive reinforcements, and reward systems, the child's confidence in their abilities grows, and this lays the foundation for more remarkable success and motivates them to develop skills. These successes replace their misconceptions about themselves, such as being disorganized, forgetful, or incompetent.

TIPS TO START A HEALTHY ROUTINE FOR YOUR CHILD

Outlined below are simple measures that you can take to help your child develop a healthy routine.

- Organize your home. Your home must be organized because having too much clutter can cause many distractions. Also, it would reflect that you do not have things under control, and the child would notice and imitate this. Keeping your home organized provides order that a child can follow. Aside from decluttering spaces and keeping things in their rightful place, you can also establish rituals around meals, homework, playtime, and bedtime.
- Involve the children in planning the routine. When children are involved in planning a schedule, they are more likely to adhere to it because of the sense of responsibility and accountability it bestows them. With input from the children, you can make the routine easy to follow, which is an effective way to help children stick to the schedule.
- Use pictures and visual cues. Children are naturally captivated by pictures. You can gain the attention and compliance of your children by using photos when making a schedule.
- Use checklists to help your child stay on task. A checklist enforces the feeling of accomplishment in children because they can easily monitor their progress and have pride in it. It also allows the children to stay focused

until completing a task. Completing tasks will also give your child a natural dopamine boost. *Dopamine* is a neurotransmitter that acts as a happy booster. People with ADHD frequently need to increase their dopamine levels as they are not as high in their brains. Often small things like finishing a task can help provide the dopamine the brain needs. Breaking tasks into smaller completable tasks can therefore make the brain even happier.

- Use a timer for daily tasks. The use of timers helps curtail distractions and keep the child focused. Set timers only for a short period because too much time leaves room for your child to become distracted. Your timers can be set for five minutes to ensure your child stays immersed in the task.
- Include breaks. Because it is harder for children with ADHD to stay focused on a task over a long period, frequent breaks are essential. Break up study sessions into shorter periods and tasks into manageable pieces.
- Limit electronic distractions. Children with ADHD are easily susceptible to distractions, including electronics like television, video games, phones, and the computer. These devices encourage impulsive behavior, and

children's exposure to them should be monitored and regulated.

- Encourage regular exercise. Research has shown that physical activity burns excess energy in healthy ways and can also help a child focus their attention. Having your child exercise regularly is an effective way to reduce impulsiveness and improve concentration.
- Set clear expectations. You must talk with your child and explain how you expect them to behave. Let them understand which behaviors are acceptable and which are not.
- Stick to the schedule and routine but allow some flexibility. It would be best if you were flexible with your child. Remember that children with ADHD do not adapt to change as quickly as others, so you must exercise patience and offer room for flexibility.
- Encourage communication with your child, both verbally and through pictographs, depending on what they respond to best. There could be days when it is impossible to stick to the routine. If you can prepare your child for this in advance, it can help them. For example, if you know that your child has a medical appointment and instead of having lunch at noon, you have to have it at eleven and then

prepare to leave for the appointment. You can let your child know earlier in the day that there will be a change to the typical routine so you can try to prepare them. Adaptations to your approach will likely be required depending on your child and how they adapt to time and a routine.

- By reinforcing your child's routine, you can help them learn that some days will not go as planned. Continually reinforcing this with your child can help them to learn that adapting will be necessary. You are doing your child an injustice if you only provide them with a routine that goes according to plan. Life does not work that way, and children must be able to adapt to unplanned changes. If your child has explosive behavior, changes in routines could cause outbursts or tantrums, but by continuing to work with them, you can defuse these behaviors before they occur.

Also note that when you start creating structure and a daily routine, especially if you have never had it before, the child may initially resist and protest against it. Still, it would help if you stuck with it while being patient yet firm; eventually, they will adjust and adopt the routine.

- Manage your own emotions. As a parent, you must learn to manage your emotions and keep yourself in check. This is important because you cannot help an impulsive child if you are easily aggravated. You must remain composed and controlled during an outburst if you expect your child also to pick up such healthy habits.

Thus, if you begin to feel angry or frustrated and feel like lashing out, remember that your child did not choose his disorder. Do not be harmful in your criticism or berate your child for mistakes or impulse behavior.

- Manage your child's emotions. Dealing with the emotional outbursts of children with ADHD can be very challenging. You must understand, firstly, though, that children with ADHD experience the same emotions as other children. However, their disorder makes their feelings more frequent, intense, and longer-lasting. Their ability to manage their emotions is affected by ADHD, and as a result of emotional dysregulation, their well-being, and success are equally affected. This also contributes to low self-esteem and social difficulties.

- Use tools such as diagrams with emotions on them to try and determine how your child is feeling. Emotional dysregulation is common in children with ADHD, but they will also experience normal emotions. Therefore, determining the underlying causes of your child's actions and emotions is essential. Working with your child to comprehend their emotions is a must. You need to see if the emotion results from their emotional dysregulation. It may also be actual sadness or anger caused by a situation. Your assessment can help your child to work through the situation. Especially if your child has explosive behavior, which causes them to lash out, it can be even more important to understand if a meltdown is the cause of overstimulation or frustration they cannot express or an underlying emotion that needs to be felt and worked through.

To help them overcome these challenges, you must help them practice gratitude and direct their attention to emotionally rewarding activities. These activities make them feel good, build a sense of pride, and increase self-esteem. When a child's self-esteem is improved, their interactions and relations with others also improve.

- Give praise and rewards. You must learn to praise and reward your child's efforts— especially when rules are followed. This is how you enforce positive behavior.

Children with ADHD often receive heavy criticism, which badly impacts their self-esteem. If you want to help your child learn and adopt positive behavior, you can start by offering kind words, hugs, or small prizes for good behavior or when they reach small goals. This motivates them to do more and increases their self-esteem and success rate.

It is also essential that all parents are committed to the routine and the plan that is placed to help their child succeed. If only one parent is committed, it can derail the other parent's efforts. This can apply in a family where the parents are together or apart. The most important thing is providing the best environment and support to a child so that they can thrive even though their ADHD comes with numerous challenges for both child and parent.

8

ADHD IN THE CLASSROOM

ADHD not only affects your child's ability to concentrate, remember, and pay attention, but it might also affect their ability to make and keep friends in school. All these factors can make you worried, and you might be concerned about how your children will cope in a regular school without being able to concentrate or with being constantly hyperactive all the time. Moreover, you are worried about how your child will enjoy going through school without having friends to play with. Worrying about this is valid, mainly because these are all critical factors that need to be addressed for your child to have the best learning experience.

If you send your child to school without prior preparation, then the chances of them having a successful school life will be low. This includes preparing your child for how to manage themselves in school and preparing yourself to be actively involved in your child's life by preparing the teachers and school authorities. This preparation will give your child a better quality of life in school by helping them to fit in completely.

School can be a major adjustment for any child, and that comes with numerous adaptations. For a child with ADHD, it can be even more difficult as school requires a lot of sitting and concentration that they likely do not have, especially if the subject is not something they are passionate about. If the child has explosive behaviors as part of their ADHD symptoms, it can be even more difficult as it can lead to lashing out or having a meltdown in the classroom or on the playground. Working on coping mechanisms at home are important because they can help the child wherever they are. You also need your child to be aware that you will not be with them at school but that they can still use the methods you have shown them. You also need to prepare the school for your child's attendance. There could also be days when your child does not go to school or must return home early because of a meltdown or being uncontrollable. Especially in the beginning, while your child builds a relationship with the teacher and trusts them for help when it comes to defusing a situation, they may be resistant to having anything to do with the teacher when they are having a difficult time regulating their emotions and behavior. Through trial and error, and the experiences that you and other teachers have had with your child, you can develop a plan to help your child and the school manage as best as possible. With each new school year, you should be prepared to speak with the professionals who will be with your child to try and create smooth transitions. Each school year also brings new routines for the child, which can take time to adapt.

MANAGING ADHD AT SCHOOL

Managing ADHD at school is always a cause for concern for parents who have children with this disorder. Although ADHD is a lifelong disorder, your child can still have a great school life if you manage it adequately.

To manage ADHD at school and create your best chance for success, you should do the following:

- Be consistent in your expectations. Consistency serves as a good safeguard against ADHD symptoms. Consistent rules and activities can help your child ease into daily school life.

Everything in school should be concise enough for them to understand.

- Limit distractions. Children with ADHD do not perform well with distractions. They must be kept on the side of the class that is void of excessive diversions. They must be seated at the front of the class or in any area with no windows or doors, which can distract them.
- Provide frequent feedback. Every child needs feedback when learning, which is even more critical for ADHD children. If they exhibit improper behavior, appropriate feedback should be given; a reward should follow if they do what is right.
- Reward them. When you reward a child with ADHD for their good behavior or for achieving set milestones, it will encourage them to continue exhibiting that good behavior. The reward you give them should be based on the things in which your child has a deep interest.
- Give breaks. ADHD children might find it challenging to focus on learning for a lengthy period. You might catch their attention drifting to several places if it becomes too long. If you want to manage them in school and keep them focused on the task, give them breaks that will

allow them to get active a little before concentrating.

- Use flexibility. If you are too rigid with a child with ADHD, you might not achieve good results. Be flexible in handling them and make some exceptions in challenging situations. You can let them hold stress balls to help them pay attention in school while pinching and squeezing.
- Avoid drowning them in schoolwork. This is counterproductive in managing the disorder. If you soak them in schoolwork, they will easily be distracted and turn towards procrastination or unhealthy outbursts of emotion. It would be best if you looked into breaking large tasks into smaller ones so they can finish quicker. If your child struggles with homework (most children with ADHD do) do not cause yourself more grief by forcing it upon your child. Find ways to be creative with it but if it becomes too much, involve the teacher to see what else can be done. The task of homework is not worth sacrificing your relationship with your child.
- Create supportive measures for them. Every child with ADHD needs support in the classroom. Having support not only includes adults but could also include fellow students. A

fellow student can be an excellent support since peers tend to understand each other better. As you pair a child who has ADHD with a child who does not struggle as much, it will help them to be less distracted and also remember pending tasks. These benefits can also lead to the blooming of a new friendship.

- In creating a plan for your child with the teacher, also be prepared to discuss appropriate discipline for your child. Oftentimes teachers will take away recess if the child misbehaves, but recess is the one time each day when a child can get their energy and wiggles out. Other disciplines should be proposed to ensure that the discipline/punishment is appropriate and can be tied to the child's behavior. Recess should never be taken away for a child with ADHD (unless there are safety issues). Instead of teaching the child how to cope with their behavior, this would actually be making their day worse and potentially causing more disruption during the day by not allowing them to get their energy out. Taking away school trips or rewards in the classroom can also be a detriment for the child. Feeling singled out or different from their classmates can lead to resentment and escalate bad behaviors.

Adaptations are always required on both sides to create the best teaching environment for the child and the other students. However, how the situation will affect the child should always be a main concern for everyone involved.

SPEAKING TO THE SCHOOL ABOUT YOUR CHILD'S BEHAVIOR

ADHD problems might not manifest in your child's behavior until they begin school. However, once they start school, you must be prepared to work alongside the school to manage their disorder so their potential can be maximized.

While your child is at school, you will not be with them the majority of the time. So, informing the school about your child's disorder is imperative. If you do not tell them, they will not know and will not give your child the support required to manage the disorder. The following sections discuss how you can ensure your child's school understands their needs.

Especially if your child has explosive behaviors as part of their ADHD symptoms, you need to explain to your child's teacher(s) what that means and how it affects your child. The key to defusing the behaviors is to ensure that everyone is prepared for what could happen. As a parent, you may have keywords or actions that you do to help your child through their explosive behaviors. Sharing these with the teacher(s) is necessary, so your child can get the support they need even when you are not present.

I have a personal experience that I want to share with you so that you know how important this communication is. My son started at a new school, and I did not inform the teachers of the techniques we use when he is upset. He did not want to get out of the car that day for school while his dad was dropping him off. They pulled out of the drop off line, and my son began hitting his dad. His dad got out of the car, and my son followed. Some teachers saw what was happening and came over. My son was really upset and walked off. He started walking in the grass, and the school could not get him to come back. He was not walking somewhere unsafe, but they felt they needed help. A school officer was there, so he came over to help. My husband called me, and I drove to the school. I had to explain to the school that I had been teaching him to remove himself from a situation if it became overwhelming. He was trying to do that, but without knowing that information, they felt he was being unsafe. After talking to my son for a few minutes, I was able to get him to agree to go with the counselor to calm down and talk about what happened. When I asked him why he would not go with the teachers before I got there, he did not want his classmates to see how upset he was. When I talked to him, I suggested meeting with the counselor to calm down before he went to his classroom. Sharing these techniques with the school would have prevented the situation from getting out of hand.

Be Enlightened

If you are unfamiliar with the laws protecting your child, how are you supposed to advocate to the school to understand what your child needs? Do your research and find out what works for your child. There are three main things for you to know that will help you give your child the best experience:

- Your child's rights.
- The support available in your child's school.
- How to prepare the school for your child's resumption.

Your Child's Rights

A behavioral plan should be created with the input of any child with ADHD. The teachers, parents, and the child should collaborate on this plan and determine the types of behavior that are unacceptable in a classroom and those that are helpful. There should be agreed-upon consequences so there are no surprises for the child or the parent. Staying in communication with the teacher is vital. Good reports are just as powerful as the ones that are not so positive.

You may be unaware that government policies protect children with disabilities at school. These laws can be found in the Individuals with Disabilities Act (IDEA) of 1975 and the Rehabilitation Act of 1973, section 504. They require that schools provide services to support the learning experience of children with disabilities. Check out my upcoming book that provides parents with clear explanation of an IEP and 504, what rights you have, what rights your child has and how to ensure you get the most of plans.

There are two plans that the government offers to the parents of children living with disabilities. These plans help the parents express the needs of the child to the school:

- Individualized education plan
- 504 plan

Individualized Education Plan (IEP)

As the name suggests, an IEP is tailored to a child's individual needs. This plan allows your child to learn alone or in smaller groups. This plan is ideal for children with different learning needs and varying learning expectations. It is also beneficial for a child that finds it hard to regulate their emotions most of the time.

This plan is very clear about the needs of the child. In addition, this plan details the child's needs to the school. However, detailing the plan to the school is not enough for a child needing special care, the plan explains the services the school will be rendering to the child. The plan also describes how the child's progress will be measured and allows the school and parents to keep track.

Having a solid IEP in place can help alleviate specific behavioral issues. If there is appropriate support, this could help your child feel less frustrated and even perform better and reduce outbursts.

504 Plan

This plan is tailored for children who have a disability but can keep up with the regular curriculum in a regular class. In addition, this option is for people whose children have little control over their emotions and impulses. Although the plan is for children that will learn with other children in the class, it still caters to their particular needs.

The document covers the needs of the child and all the necessary steps the school must take to support them. Remember, your child will be learning the same thing as their classmates; the difference is how your child is treated regarding the school activities. Common ways the school might bend the typical activities for your child include the following:

- Take verbal tests instead of written ones. As your child deals with ADHD, it might become hard for them to focus on written tests and lose focus every few minutes. Due to this, they will be more likely to focus when listening than reading. When they take oral tests, it will be easier to call their attention back when they are beginning to lose focus and latch onto irrelevant things. This program will allow them to take oral tests to ensure they are on track and do not fail because of their hyperactivity or inability to focus.

- Typically students with ADHD struggle to both listen and write, so having one less task to do so that they can focus on the lesson being taught is helpful. Therefore, if the teacher can provide worksheets that have already been completed, the student will have one less thing to need to try to concentrate on. This can significantly improve their chances of succeeding. I have seen this to be of great help when both of my children are in class and preparing for a test. As the teacher is reviewing and preparing for the test, most children would fill in the blanks. This suggestion is the teacher provides them the sheet that already has the answers completed so your child can focus on what the teacher is saying.

- Get audio textbooks instead of written ones. In most schools, textbooks are readily available to all the students, but only in exceptional cases will a student get a text in audio format. This plan takes care of this, as it informs the school about the child's need for audio textbooks for optimized learning. These audio textbooks help the child to enjoy reading. Since they would enjoy studying because they can hear rather than read, it will prevent boredom which causes a lack of focus.
- Take tests in a room with less stimulation. Since your child will be learning in a typical classroom setup, many distractions will occur. A typical classroom has charts, drawings, colors, sounds, many other students, and usually windows. Anything can cause your child to lose focus in class. It could be the color of a classmate's backpack, the type of shoe the teacher wore, the trees blowing outside, or even a chart hanging up nearby that can cause

distractions. These distractions can hinder your child's success at being able to focus on classwork or tests. Your child might have impressive knowledge of test content but immediately get distracted and struggle to focus on what they were doing. When children get frustrated and are not able to focus and are up against a time limit, this could increase the chances of the child getting upset and into a situation where they become emotional.

This plan eliminates this problem. It prepares the school for your child's needs on tests, explaining how hyperactive and easily distracted they might be. This helps the school prepare a classroom where your child can take tests. Since they know your child's needs, they will ensure that the room is plain without so many distractions in sight so that your child can comfortably take their test.

- Some children experience time blindness, so giving them more time will be ineffective. However, breaking the test or schoolwork into smaller pieces and allowing for breaks in between might be the answer. The breaks might be the necessary measure for keeping the child on task while they need to work. This does not

ADHD IN THE CLASSROOM | 133

mean they might not still lose focus but reminding them that there is another ten minutes before a break might help to bring them back to the task.

- This plan covers this need, as you do not need to be worried about your child spacing out or needing more time to finish tests or exams. This plan will let the school know that your child cannot simultaneously complete these tests and exams with other children, even if kept in a separate room. They will also understand that your child needs enough time to finish things properly. This plan will let the schools guide your child at their own pace.

The Support Available in Your Child's School

The support available in schools varies and depends on the school. Apart from knowing your child's rights and relating them to the school, you must know the specific services your child's school provides for students like your child. Ask the principal of your child's school about the services available to your child. Take your questions seriously. Ask them what services they have to make your child comfortable with being at school and what will give your child the best chances of being successful. Ask them how they can help your child become socially inclined without disrupting school life.

Some schools teach small groups of children basic social skills by letting this small group of three to seven students intermingle until they get used to each other. The school psychologist or therapist often leads the groups. These groups will enlighten your child on how to behave in social situations and how to talk with their peers. In addition, it teaches the child basic conversational skills.

HOW TO PREPARE THE SCHOOL FOR YOUR CHILD'S ATTENDANCE

It is not enough to have a plan and know the school's services; you must understand how to prepare the school for your child's attendance. It is easy when dealing with an old school because you do not need to go above and beyond in preparation. However, if it is a new school, you have to get the school acquainted with your child and vice versa before your child's attendance. If you do not do that, everything will seem strange to your child when they go to school, and the school might find it hard to help your child keep up with other students. Therefore, to prepare the school for your child's presence, you must contact the school and tell them your concerns.

Explain to them how your child learns so they can assign your child to a teacher that matches their ability.

You can also arrange with the school to keep your child in a class more suitable for their learning abilities. For example, some classes can be noisy and too overstimulating for your child, so before school starts, you can get the chance to pick the class that you feel is more suitable for your child.

In addition to preparing the school for your child's arrival, it is necessary to prepare your child with ADHD for the upcoming school year, whether it is in a new school or a different classroom. By preparing your child in advance, you can help work on any anxieties or stresses they might feel about the routine changes. Adequate preparedness can help smooth the transition as it can greatly reduce the likelihood of your child experiencing explosive behaviors such as meltdowns. Talking about the new school or classroom and using pictograms or photos to initiate the conversation and discuss the changes can be effective techniques for helping your child get ready for the new school year. After school breaks, such as longer holidays like Christmas, you should also be preparing your child for their return a few days in advance.

Before school begins, your child can meet the essential people in the school that they will see every day and prepare your child to interact with them. It also helps that there are familiar faces your child will see once school resumes. Some people you might arrange for your child to introduce themselves to include your child's teachers, the nurse, the psychologist or guidance counselor, the speech therapist (if the school has one), and the principal.

The people your child needs to see before school begins depends on how often these people will be around your child. If these people will not be around your child often, then there is no need for your child to meet them. Instead, the reason your child is meeting them is to ensure that there is a comfortable atmosphere when your child sees them at the beginning of school.

If you are worried your child might have trouble connecting with other students, you can set up a play-date. This playdate can consist of two other children in your child's peer group. During this playdate, your child can get to know these children and even become friends with them. Even though they will have a play-date, ensure they are supervised so you can let your child rest when they are overly emotional.

Meeting with people is one part of school preparation; the other is letting your child get acquainted with the environment. It is not enough to know people at school. If your child does not know their way around the school, it might be detrimental to their experience. So, you can choose a person that will spend lots of time with your child in school to accompany you and your child around the school. It might be the school's nurse or therapist. Whatever you choose, the person should accompany you to places your child needs to go. This will give your child a sense of familiarity at the beginning of the school year.

HOW TEACHERS CAN HELP

Teachers play a significant role in your child's ability to fit in with a class. If your child's teachers know what they are dealing with, it will be easy for them to help your child. Unfortunately, with ADHD, your child will also find it difficult to explain themselves to the teacher, making it quite difficult for the teacher to know what is wrong. Since ADHD symptoms differ from person to person, it would be better for you to elaborate on your child's symptoms so the teacher can use appropriate methods to ensure they are successful. The ways you can talk to the teachers to get them to help are explained below.

Schedule an Appointment with the Teacher

You might think it is easy to breeze into the school and have a quick unannounced talk with the teacher, but it is not. If you choose to talk to the teacher after school, the school might be in rush hour, so your conversation would have several distractions and would not be very beneficial. If you meet up with the teacher before school begins, it might be similar to the previous option. The teacher might be rushing to get back to class, and you might also be time conscious because of work. It is also important to respect the teacher's time as they may be unavailable and have a previous commitment.

What is the use of two people attempting a meaningful discussion if their minds are elsewhere? A conversation where both minds are unsettled is pointless. For a delicate discussion about your child's education, you and the teacher must be fully attentive to avoid missing important details. Therefore, make an appointment with the teacher and choose an appropriate time that you would be free to discuss. The length of time does not matter because as little as twenty minutes is enough to discuss the important details.

If there are no distractions, then a little time is enough to let the teacher understand the details. You can set the appointment before resuming school or during school; the selected time does not matter. All that matters is that you set an appointment to review the details thoroughly.

Explain the Meaning of ADHD

Although the teacher is well educated, they might not know what ADHD truly means. There is no doubt that they might have heard about ADHD, but there is a possibility that they do not know a lot about it. Sometimes people tend to have more misconceptions about a disorder than facts. Due to this, the teacher might only have a vague understanding of ADHD.

This is not out of the ordinary; many believe that ADHD is a mental health disorder that can be cured. While discussing with the teacher, you are gradually becoming a guide that will help them understand the disorder. Although some teachers might have had students with ADHD under their care, not many truly understand the intricacies involved, especially as each child is different. You are most aware of your child's ADHD symptoms and behaviors. Your knowledge can be a powerful resource to the teacher. Make sure you respect the teacher and do not assume they know nothing about ADHD but do not assume they know everything. Provide education in regard to ADHD for how it relates to your child.

Explain the ADHD Symptoms in Relation to Your Child

Explaining how ADHD most affects your child to their teacher is a significant step toward helping them understand and take care of your child. However, it is not enough to tell them about it; you must elaborate on your child's ADHD. Only when you discuss ADHD with your child's teacher will it no longer seem like a lecture. Telling your child's teacher about ADHD is explanatory but, at the same time, vague because many symptoms of ADHD vary from person to person. The fact that your child has emotional outbursts because of their disorder does not mean every other child managing that disorder suffers the same. The symptoms of ADHD in each child are different, so if your explanation is vague, the teacher might be looking to help with the wrong aspects of your child's behavior.

Be specific about the symptoms that your child experiences. For example, if your child experiences daydreaming, you can explain it to the teacher. As the teacher learns about your child's symptoms, they become aware of what to look for when in the classroom. Through the symptoms, they begin to observe your child better to ensure that your child achieves great academic excellence. Talk about everything you know about your child's disorder, as leaving out any detail will not be helpful. If your child has negative coping mechanisms like lying or irrational outbursts of emotions, it will be better to explain that to the teacher. The more information provided to the teacher, the better because it will help the teacher be prepared should the behaviors occur in the classroom. Sharing your methods for dealing with the situation can also help. Perhaps you have certain words that you say to your child to help them calm down after a meltdown. You could use a fidget toy or stress ball to help them pay attention or refocus them when they need to listen. Simple actions that will not disrupt the rest of the class but work to keep your child on task can benefit everyone involved in the care of your child.

Tell the Teacher About Your Child's Current Plan

Telling your child's teacher about the type of plan your child is on is crucial. Even though the teacher knows about the symptoms, a good understanding of your child's plan will help the teacher take the proper steps to ensure a good learning atmosphere for them. It is best not to be vague about your child's plan. Saying your child is on an IEP or 504 plan is not enough information for the teacher to know what has been discussed and agreed to.

To better understand the topic, bring a printed copy of the plan so they can understand the intricacies and how they can adapt their teaching plan or style to meet your child's standards. Remember to explain to the teacher that these requirements do not mean your child should be excluded from the school curriculum. Instead, explain that you want your child to meet school expectations; these are the only requirements that will improve their learning and help them reach their highest potential.

Communicating with your child's teachers is necessary beyond their ability to complete schoolwork. It would help if you spoke with them about what can trigger certain behaviors in your child. They are at the school for a full day, including recess, lunch hour, and physical education classes. All of these things can have triggers for your child. Making your teacher fully aware of your child's ADHD symptoms and behaviors is necessary so the school can help your children. For example, the lunchroom may trigger your child because it is too noisy. Maybe the noise causes your child to be anxious and become overwhelmed, which could lead to a meltdown or a tantrum. Let the teacher and lunch hour supervisors know this so they can try to help your child. Wearing a set of earplugs can help your child in this situation, and the teacher/staff at the school can remind your child to use them if they are struggling. Often solutions for helping a child deal with their emotional regulation can be simple as long as everyone is prepared for the possible outcomes and has some ideas of solutions they can use to deal with the situation.

Talk About the Strategies You Have Used With The Child

The talk with your child's teacher can be considered complete if you talk about the strategies you have used in the past. Also, whether the strategies worked or not is not important. The main thing is communication so that the right strategies can be used. It will be best for you to tell the teacher every strategy you might have tried. That way, the teacher will have an insight into your struggles and a glimpse of what they should or should not try. If your child experiences explosive behavior, the coping mechanisms you have used to defuse these situations must also be shared. Perhaps what works for you is providing the child with a specific tool, such as a stress ball, to help them calm down. It could be singing them a song or a key phrase that you use to help empower them. Every detail shared, whether it be little or big, is beneficial. No detail is insignificant when communicating with your child's teacher about your child's ADHD, so do not forget to share all the failed strategies. The details you share are beneficial if it concerns your child's behavior and how it relates to their education.

Be Open to Hearing the Teacher's Opinion

You are conversing with your child's teacher rather than instructing them. Doing all the talking will make you feel like you are instructing the teacher. So, how

144 | ROSE LYONS

about you ask for the teacher's thoughts on what you said? If you do all the talking, you may never know the wealth of knowledge the teacher has or the areas they need help understanding. Ask them what ideas they have about dealing with your child's behavior. Some teachers have worked with children who have behavioral issues, so they might have first-hand experience that you will find helpful.

Due to asking their opinions, you might find out something about behavioral management you did not know. They might offer management skills that work for other children. Their suggestions might intrigue you and might be what your child needs. You see how well they understand these things as you let them talk. Hearing the teacher's opinions will put the teacher's mind at ease, as well as yours, after understanding that they are on the same page as you and willing to go out of their way to help your child succeed.

Show Interest in Partnering with the Teacher

Your child's teacher will be happier to work with you if they realize that you are willing to partner with them or help them manage your child's school affairs. Asking them how you can help indicates that you trust them to do a good job, but you are also interested in making their job easier. In addition, every teacher who sees a parent willing to help their child succeed at school will be happy.

So, this will be good news for both parties—you and the teacher. You could always show your interest in wanting to help out by keeping in touch with the teacher. It would help if you chose a platform where it will be easy for both parties to talk, including emails, text messages, or any other messaging platform you agree on. As you regularly talk to the teacher, you will be informed regularly about your child's behavior, and rarely will things get out of hand before you notice.

HOW TO WORK ALONGSIDE THE TEACHERS

Working alongside teachers is necessary for a parent with a child managing any disorder. It is easy to work with teachers, but you might offend the teacher and make them shut down with a wrong move. Remember now that you and the teacher are on one team and working towards a goal together. You must think of what approach you will take with the teacher.

- Talk carefully. If you are not tactful while speaking, you might say something that offends the teacher or puts them on the defensive. This is why choosing your words wisely is imperative, especially when you need help getting answers or the help you plan to get. Please do not say you are blaming the teacher or insinuating that they are not doing their job. Instead of asking them why something is wrong, rephrase your question as you are concerned and willing to help. When you do this, the teacher will not always be guarded around you.

- Do not be defensive. There will be times when issues about your child will be brought up. There are times your child might cause a stir in school. You know how your child can behave; therefore, even if these reports come to you and seem like something your child is incapable of, you should listen attentively.

Do not lash out or be unnecessarily defensive. Instead, only discuss the way forward and steps to avoid such actions from your child. Commend the teachers for their efforts in curbing your child's excesses. When you do this, the teacher will strive to help your child perform at their best, knowing that you support them.

- Keep the teacher informed. As much as you regularly keep in touch with the teacher, asking about your child's performance in school, it would help if you kept the teacher informed.

The information passing back and forth between you and the teacher is the key to optimal breakthroughs. Sometimes, situations at home that may be considered normal or unimportant can affect a child more than we know.

Change is constant; therefore, you must understand how to manage the change. In this case, managing change involves communication. Tell the teacher about the change in ADHD medications, if any. If there is a death in the family or a separation/divorce, also inform the teacher because these changes can affect the child's behavior. Informing the teacher will make them prepared to handle any situation arising.

- Work on shared goals. When you and the teacher meet one-on-one, you should encourage working on shared goals. Your goal is to effectively manage your child's disorder; however, managing it alone in school is ineffective. Working on shared goals will help you and the teacher monitor your child's progress and work together to encourage the development and ultimate management of ADHD.

- Take parent-teacher meetings seriously. Parent-teacher meetings usually are brief, so taking them seriously is essential. Attend every one because they are necessary to learn more about your child's progress in school. Also, ensure you are prepared because you must be organized to remember what you might have been eager to ask. Before you go, you must list all the questions that need to be answered on paper, so you remember them. Remember to organize report cards, teacher's notes, and every other school item of great importance.

- Volunteer. Volunteering is imperative if you are trying to work side-by-side with the teacher and your child. You can pitch in as a chaperone if the school is going on a trip. Doing this will give you a glimpse into your child's behavior in school. It will also make the teacher see how immersed you are in the school affairs of your child. In most cases, your child might be happy to see you there even though they do not interact with you much.

- Appreciate the teacher. Never underestimate the importance of appreciation. Appreciation can make a person continue what they do because they are happy that their efforts were acknowledged. Similarly, if you appreciate the teacher, they will be more comfortable doing more for your child. Do not appreciate them just because you read that here; appreciate them from your heart because you believe they have done a great job. If a teacher goes a mile or two to understand your child, they deserve to be thanked. There are different ways you can appreciate them. Sometimes, a small thank you note on their table might make them smile. A gift can be great too. The appreciation depends on what you can do and afford.

9

NAVIGATING SOCIAL SKILLS

Social skills play an important part in our lives as humans. Social skills encompass all the skills from verbal (speed of speech, volume, and tone of speech) to non-verbal (facial expression, body language, and eye contact), enabling us to interact and communicate with others. Unfortunately, due to executive dysfunction, children with ADHD might find it hard to use these social skills and act inappropriately in social interaction.

Some inappropriate behaviors that will put off their peers when interacting with them include:

- missing social cues
- being inattentive and missing several pieces of information

- being easily distracted by sounds
- Having difficulty listening to others for long periods
- frequently interrupting while conversing with others
- talking fast or too much
- being highly focused on one topic
- having disordered thoughts
- sharing thoughts in a disordered manner
- initiating conversations at inappropriate times
- displaying aggression or lack of emotional control
- lacking boundaries and being unaware of others' personal space

Your child might engage in inattentive, hyperactive, and impulsive behaviors that drive other children away. Your child might miss social cues necessary to make a friend; even when they make one, they might be too distracted by little things and miss important information shared by their friend. This behavior offends adults as well as children. If a person does not listen and you keep repeating one thing over and over again, it makes you feel like they are not interested in being your friend. In many cases, the other child will back out from initiating a friendship.

They might also find it hard to listen to their friends for long periods, which can put their friends off. If they have a friend who listens to them rant and talks uncoordinatedly, it is normal for the friend to expect the same thing from them. If the friend expects them to listen and they do not, they might appear rude or insensitive. Since conversation is a two-way street, people find it disrespectful for a person to be the only one talking without letting them say their views. No one will remain friends with a person that is constantly interrupting them. Having disordered thoughts is one thing, but voicing those thoughts is another and genuinely a put-off.

Children with ADHD, especially if they display explosive behaviors, might also be triggered to have a meltdown or show some aggression, like hitting in a social situation that is not going their way. Sometimes simple things like the other child doing something different in a game that the child is used to playing with someone else might be enough to make their explosive behaviors appear. Being overwhelmed can be another reason that the child may show these behaviors. On the playground, for example, a lot can happen with the activity that your child and their friend are doing and what the other children are doing. Your child might be on the swings with their friend and looking over at the soccer field, the slide, monkey bars, etc. Working with your

154 | ROSE LYONS

child to prepare them for social situations and all the feelings that can come from their condition is important. This behavior can be frightening for the child they are trying to befriend, and it will also be difficult for your child. It can be helpful to have a conversation with the parent of the child your child is trying to befriend to explain some of the behaviors to the new friend. That way, a plan can be implemented to benefit everyone. The solution might be for the friend to seek out the assistance of an adult in order to help manage behaviors.

Respecting personal space is one of the keys to maintaining friendships. However, if your child does not understand personal space and keeps invading others' space at school, it might be hard for them to have friends. Initiating conversations at the wrong times, even when they have been told not to, is another negative social skill that might affect their ability to make friends. However, the scariest of the negative social skills is the display of aggression and lack of emotional control. If your child lacks emotional control, other children might not want to come close for fear of being poorly treated.

The above factors represent various reasons your child might struggle to make friends or maintain long-lasting friendships. However, do not worry; there are tips for helping your child socialize and have a successful social life.

Also, try these methods for short time frames and with small groups, at least initially. Children with ADHD, especially if they are prone to explosive behaviors, can easily become overwhelmed, and this can create an undesirable situation. It will all depend on the child and how noises and situations affect them when it comes to what they can handle. For some children with ADHD, being in a social situation can be difficult since their executive dysfunction might cause them to hear every little sound around them, which can be overwhelming. The right place and people are essential to your child's social interactions. If possible, try to get your child to explain how they felt once you are home so that you can adapt social situations in the future to their specific needs.

TIPS TO HELP YOUR CHILD SOCIALIZE BETTER

- Provide immediate feedback about miscues and inappropriate behaviors. ADHD might make your child lack self-awareness; hence, they might not know when they are doing inappropriate things around their peers. Help

your children learn the importance of being
social, such as greeting their friends when they
meet them in public, or saying please and thank
you when they ask for a toy or sporting
equipment at recess. Some behaviors can be
off-putting to others. However, you can work
to improve these situations through role play,
pictograms, and conversations with your
children. Positively reinforcing good behavior
can also help. When possible, reinforce the
behaviors right away. Also, be sure to be clear in
letting your child know what behaviors you are
proud of so they know what to strive for. For
example, instead of just saying a good job, you
might say good job sharing the ball when you
play. Ensuring connection is vital in helping
your child achieve their full potential in all life
situations.

- Focus on strengthening the areas that your
child struggles with the most. The fact that your
child has ADHD does not mean they will have
problems with all areas of their life. They might
have issues with emotional control but
understand personal space. The areas a child
with ADHD will need help with depends on the
child. Since you know your child and the

possible areas that might be a problem, focus on them rather than general issues.

- Playdates are important. Playdates are important when trying to develop your child's social skills. Since children with ADHD will thrive better in smaller gatherings than in larger ones, a playdate of ten children might be counterproductive. Instead, it will be preferred if the playdate consists of at most four children. This will help your child to socialize effectively without social anxiety.
- Reward them accordingly. If your child displays appropriate behaviors during a playdate or uses new social skills successfully, reward them immediately. This encourages them to keep up that good behavior. You can reward them for making a new friend unassisted and reward them when they have successful playdates.
- Communicate with your child often. Communication reveals so much that we might not have guessed. Many children with ADHD face bullying and other types of adversity in school. Even while facing these situations, they might not tell anyone or say they forgot when you find out. Many children like this are the bully's target, so if you do not talk to your child,

you might not know the underlying cause of your child's disorder.

- Prepare your child for social interactions. Preparations are always important for a child with ADHD. You have to ease them into a routine before they can get used to it. It would be best to create real-life scenarios at home that mimic what they might encounter eventually. When you do this, teach them how to respond by asking them what they think about certain situations. Guide them where they need guidance. You could also watch movies with your child and ask them what they think about some characters. You should also prepare your child for playdates, so they do not do and say the wrong things. You can teach them how to manage conflict that might arise during the playdates so that they will control their emotions when it happens.

- Encourage your child to take notes. Since children with ADHD might forget many details because of their attention span, encourage them to take notes on their friends' names and other important facts, they think they might forget. This will help them remember these details when they interact with their friends.

- Teach your child about boundaries. Boundaries are an important part of our lives. If you teach your child about boundaries by speaking to them when you notice that they overstepped, you can help them understand how important it is to respect others' personal space.
- Be prepared to take time outs from social interaction. Even at a playdate, a child can become overwhelmed even if, just minutes before, it seemed like they were having fun. Calling a break when your child appears to be getting distracted or suggesting that the children switch to a quieter activity if you sense your child is becoming overstimulated can be helpful. You may also want to set time limits for activities with friends. Even a thirty-minute to an hour playdate might be plenty for your child to handle, especially in the beginning. Especially if your child displays explosive behaviors, you want to keep things from reaching that point. Through work with your child, you will hopefully be able to help them learn when to identify that they need a break. The more you communicate with your child and work with them on finding solutions to their behaviors, the better their chances for positive interactions with others.

- Sign your child up for team sports. Although individual sports can benefit children with ADHD, team sports can also be great. If they play these sports, they might learn teamwork, improving their social skills. For some children, team sports might be out of the question. For example, if your child with ADHD is triggered to have explosive behavior when the whistle goes off or there is too much cheering from the crowd, it might not be the best option. Some children are too distracted by a lot of activity to succeed in a larger group setting, such as on a soccer team. Exploring other options, such as playing badminton, might be an option, as there are fewer people to interact with. Plenty of studies show that activities such as horseback riding can be extremely therapeutic for children with ADHD. Your child's teammate does not necessarily have to be a person. They can make friends with animals which can help to boost their confidence levels too. Also, children with ADHD are often known to hyperfocus on their interests. Therefore finding activities that interest them could be the key to having them interact in a group setting. For example, if your child loves art, drawing classes might be a good option for them. There has

been lots of research about the benefits of art
therapy too.

- Praise them for good behavior. Children with
  ADHD deal with many emotional problems.
  Due to their social challenges, they might also
  have reduced self-esteem. If you praise them
  when you see them exhibit good behaviors, you
  will boost their self-esteem and make them
  strive to manage their symptoms better.

SOCIAL SKILLS GROUP

Social skills group is a group that enhances the social
life of children and adolescents that are enrolled. Since
children with ADHD find it difficult to fit in with their
peers, they might need extra training to learn how to
act appropriately in social situations and become
capable of handling conversations, friendships, and
conflicts.

How They Work

This group handles social life's nonverbal and verbal
aspects and merges them to help the child become
socially comfortable interacting with their peers. These
groups teach the child how to communicate verbally
with other people. It ensures the child understands
appropriate and inappropriate things to say to people

in various situations. It also teaches the child about nonverbal communication, like how to interpret body language and facial expressions. Interpreting body language and facial expressions will help the child understand when they are doing things at inappropriate times or creeping into someone's personal space and the person is upset.

How to Create One

Professionals create a social skills group based not on diagnostic history but on the child's social skills. Although it is created based on the child's social skills, it is also age appropriate. A social skills group cannot consist of a seven-year-old child and another thirteen; it does not work that way. Group leaders are flexible in their group creation to ensure their training impacts the children. These professionals use different means like modeling, role-playing, and teaching. Training is practiced over a long period until the child has a grip on it.

10

MEDICATING

I t is sometimes a struggle to choose between medications and other therapies. As a parent, this decision might make you stall for several months before taking the next step. Delaying before deciding to use medication to control your child's ADHD is not bad. It is essential to consult your health professional to know if your child should begin using medication. Their advice is also crucial in understanding the suitable times for starting these medications. Sharing all information about your child's behaviors is necessary when choosing the right option with your child's healthcare provider. You may want to keep a log of their behaviors to share with your doctor. The right medications or treatments could depend on how often certain things happen. For example, there is a difference if your child has daily, weekly, or monthly explosive behaviors. If a situation happens infrequently, medication might not be needed for that specific ADHD symptom.

Keeping track of how a medication affects a child after receiving it is also important so the medical professional can determine if the child has the right medication for their specific situation. You should also frequently ask others with your child for feedback. For example, their teacher can let you know if behaviors in the classroom have changed.

ADHD MEDICATIONS

The medications used in treating ADHD are divided into two branches according to their effect on the central nervous system. The branches are:

- stimulant medications
- non-stimulant medication

Stimulant Medications

Stimulant medications are popularly prescribed for ADHD by medical personnel. Their action is to increase the amount of dopamine (known as the happy hormone) and the amount of norepinephrine in the central nervous system. The action of these medications calms the central nervous system and reduces hypersensitivity. This will provide your child with calmness and proper concentration. Discussed below are some examples of stimulant medications.

- Amphetamine-based stimulants: These stimulants are made from Amphetamine, the most popular type of stimulant. Some examples of these stimulants are:

  - Adderall
  - Dextrostat
  - Dexedrine

- Dextromethamphetamine stimulants: The most popular type of this stimulant is Desoxyn.
- Dexmethylphenidate stimulants: The most common type of this stimulant prescribed for ADHD is Focalin.
- Methylphenidate stimulants: These stimulants are derivatives of methylphenidate, and examples of this class of stimulants are:

  - Concerta
  - Daytrana
  - Metadate

- Ritalin

Non-Stimulant Medications

This option is used when there is no significant improvement after administering stimulant medications. These medications are also used when stimulant medications have substantial, lasting side effects.

There is no exact knowledge about the actions of most ADHD non-stimulant medications in the central nervous system. However, four non-stimulant medications are indicated as medications that stimulate the release of norepinephrine in the nervous system to bring calmness and concentration to the user.

- Strattera (an Atomoxetine derivative)
- Pamelor (antidepressant-like nortriptyline)
- Intuniv (guanfacine)
- Kapvay (clonidine)

ALTERNATIVE MEDICATIONS

The medications used to manage ADHD in children are not limited to stimulants and non-stimulants; your physician can prescribe other medications depending on your child's disorder and the most suitable option available. The two classes of medications used in place of stimulants and non-stimulants are:

- Antidepressants
- Anti-hypertensives

UPSIDES OF ADHD MEDICATIONS

Although you might consider the side effects when using medication for ADHD, there are significant benefits your child will reap that you cannot ignore. These benefits span all types of ADHD medication. They include:

- reduction of hyperactivity
- increase of motivation
- increase in productivity
- reduction of procrastination
- increase in attention span
- the manageable pace of thoughts
- decrease of impulsivity
- improvement in school performance
- promotion of a better social life
- increase in the ability to focus for more extended periods

THE DOWNSIDES OF ADHD MEDICATIONS

Many people are skeptical about using medications to treat ADHD because of the potential side effects that might follow. Of course, every drug has its side effects, but side effects are drug dependent. Still, some common side effects might occur while using stimulants and non-stimulants to control your child's ADHD. Outlined below are some common side effects:

- headache
- insomnia
- upset stomach
- nervousness
- irritability
- loss of weight
- dry mouth

The common side effects can be present in stimulants and non-stimulants. These side effects may not need a trip to the doctor every day and can be easy to deal with. However, severe side effects might need urgent attention, although they rarely occur. The serious side effects also depend on the class of the drug used.

Severe side effects that may accompany the use of stimulants are:

- auditory or visual hallucinations (hearing or seeing things that are not real)
- blood pressure increase
- allergic reaction
- suicidal actions back up the contemplation of suicide that may or may not

Severe side effects that may accompany the use of non-stimulants are:

- seizures
- suicidal actions back up the contemplation of suicide that may or may not

Understanding that these side effects do not occur in typical cases is imperative. It is rare for the side effects of stimulants and non-stimulants to reach this level of severity.

SHOULD YOU MEDICATE?

Before reading this, you might have been aware that side effects could follow the use of these medications.

After reading about these side effects, you might wonder if it is a good idea to start or continue using medication. Unfortunately, several decisions plague parents' minds when deciding whether to use medications as therapy for their children with ADHD.

Some parents fear these medications will make their children behave like mindless zombies. You might feel the medication will stunt the child's true personality but is that the case? With medication, a child might not be as active as they used to be, but that does not mean they have lost their personality. This new development means the child is aware of the appropriate actions instead of mindlessly being hyperactive.

You might also worry about your child becoming dependent on the medication. Your child having to use their medication does not mean they are automatically addicted. Instead, the medicine is like a pillar they can fall back on to make them feel better. It is very similar to the way we drink water. It is a feedback mechanism where we experience thirst and take water to quench it. This analogy is similar to a child that has ADHD using their medications. They are not addicted. They need it to have a better quality of life.

Another concern might be why medication is an option while there are other therapeutic ways to manage

ADHD. The reason why medication might be advised to you is plausible. Not every situation can be handled using a natural approach. For example, if you want to align your teeth to have the perfect dentition, you might decide to wait it out and hope your teeth straighten naturally. But how many times have you seen that work? Even children in middle school must wear braces to straighten their teeth out rather than wait for nature to take its course.

Braces are unnatural, but they serve their purpose perfectly well. This is similar to taking ADHD medications. You can choose natural therapy, but if your child's hyperactivity continues, the doctor might ask you to take medication. To manage the disorder medicine can make a substantial difference in managing ADHD. Even the natural therapies that you might be more inclined to are not perfect and might not give you the effect you are looking for.

Another thought that might plague your mind when considering the suitability of medication is believing that you might have failed as a parent. If you have this thought, it would be wise to discard it from your mind before you start feeling like it is true. Giving your child medications for ADHD does not mean you are lazy or have failed as a parent. Contrary to what you might think, you are helping your child become the best version of themselves. Do not think you are doing it to relieve yourself of dealing with your child's ADHD because you know deep down that you want your child to live a healthy and happy life.

Think of medication like you are helping your child eliminate the burden of not being able to concentrate. Instead of guilt-tripping yourself, pat yourself on the back because you are trying your best to ensure your child has a better quality of life.

The thought of beginning medication alone might be overwhelming. Sometimes, when faced with challenges, we might want to back out of what seems like an arduous task. You might be thinking of all the trips you must take to the doctor's office. You might also wonder about the numerous tests your child will need to undergo and the medications they will need to try to choose the most suitable one. In a world where every parent is busy and trying to create a favorable environment for their children, frequent trips to the doctor to run countless tests might not seem like a great idea.

If you are a parent that has tried other therapies to manage your child's ADHD, you might be wary of introducing medications into the treatment. You might think, "If this has worked so far, why do I still need to use medications while treating my child?" It is imperative to remember that as a person ages, their needs also grow. If you compare how you were when you were little and how you are now, you will notice that your needs are more significant and different. For example, consider changes in your appetite; a small bowl of cereal when you were little might not fill you at thirty. This is the same with the growth of a child. The child's needs at five would differ from their needs at twelve. As they grow, their needs grow too.

Remember, ADHD is a lifelong disorder, so sufficient treatment in previous years might not be enough in later years. If natural therapy was adequate in treating a child of seven, you might need to do it alongside medication by the time they are fourteen. Naturally, the older they get, the more responsibilities they will have and the more executive functions they need. Although your child survived only on natural therapy in grade school, they might need to add medication in high school when they have calculus and arithmetic to concentrate on. Adding medication simply helps your child focus so they can identify their strengths and weaknesses. It is never too late or too early to begin medication; if prescribed, be assured that it will improve the quality of your child's life.

Whether you choose to medicate or not is in your hands. It is not mandatory to use natural means, just as it is not compulsory to use medications to manage ADHD. No textbooks or rules say that if you do not medicate your child, they will not have a good quality of life. Diving into medication the minute your child is diagnosed with ADHD is unnecessary. If you decide to begin medicating your child immediately, you must weigh your options and reasons for medicating above other options. You must determine if you are choosing medication from the start to improve executive function or reduce excessive hyperactivity, which can cause emotional instability and impulsive actions.

Weighing your options will let you know the most suitable for your child. For example, suppose you choose not to start medicating from the onset of the diagnosis but have consistently found relief from other approaches. In that case, you might eventually need to use the medication and the non-medication options you already use. Regardless of which option you choose to manage your child's ADHD, you might need to complement it with others. Using the two options will lead your child to a more relaxed state. Although they are both valid, you must discuss the best option for your child with your physician.

ADHD THERAPY

Therapy for this diagnosis refers to the other methods (sans medication) that can be combated without medication. Again, discussing with your doctor whether this will be a better option for you is crucial. The methods of therapy include:

- psychotherapy
- social training skills
- parental and teacher training skills
- support groups

Psychotherapy

Psychotherapy is the use of psychological means in treating ADHD. Psychotherapy will help your child monitor behavior patterns and choose to act correctly. Typically, psychotherapy is done in two phases:

- behavior therapy
- cognitive behavioral therapy (CBT)

Behavior Therapy

In behavior therapy, the psychologist guides the parent and child on scrutinizing the child's behaviors. The use of scrutiny will help identify the details of behaviors that require change. A positive feedback mechanism will change the child's behavior gradually. The positive feedback mechanism depends on the suggestion of the psychologist. For example, the psychologist might recommend a reward following a positive behavior from your child.

Cognitive Behavioral Therapy

This type of therapy aims to rectify adverse thinking patterns that are often associated with this disorder. One significant negative thinking pattern is perfection. If they do not perceive a thing done by someone with ADHD to be perfect, they might lose motivation. As motivation is lost, the next step is to ignore the task or procrastinate. Instead of doing this, cognitive behavioral therapy will teach them to change this mindset of perfection or nothing.

Social Training Skills

Sometimes, people with ADHD have limited social skills because of their inability to focus. This social training will help to suppress bouts of energy that might seem impossible to control previously. As a result, they will experience a healthier social life at school and home as they learn to control some of these behaviors.

Parental and Teacher Training Skills

As a parent, there are skills that you need to manage a child with ADHD. Parental skills give you insight into what you are dealing with and a thorough understanding of managing the disorder. With these skills, you will handle each aspect with ease. Teachers also need these skills to manage the child's ADHD symptoms. The following skills and therapeutic measures will give your child the quality of life they deserve.

- Reward system: The reward system is an important strategy for managing your child. You have to know what your child loves, which can serve as a reward. Also, you must monitor your child's behavior to note when they have good behavior at home or school. For every excellent behavior they exhibit, it is imperative to reward them with their favorite thing (could be snacks or toys). You cannot carry out this system alone, so you might need the teacher's help. The teacher could monitor your child's behavior in school and give you daily feedback about the positive and negative behaviors your child exhibits. Then, depending on their behavior, you can decide whether to reward them for the day.

- Healthy meals: Believe it or not, healthy meals play a vital role in managing many health disorders. Your child's disorder can quickly improve or take a downhill turn depending on their diet. A healthy meal is a balanced diet with each nutrient your child needs. Never neglect your child's nutritional needs because it could worsen things. A study showed a lower level of omega-3 fatty acids in children with ADHD. The interaction between ADHD and Omega-3 fatty acids is not clear. Still, you can mix up your child's diet with fruits, whole grains, vegetables, and fish (which could be a source of omega -3 fatty acids for your child) or other proteins. There is little research on the appropriate meals for ADHD children, but if you have any concerns, you could talk to your health provider. Dopamine is also extremely important for your child. In someone with an ADHD deficiency, the level of this neurotransmitter in their brain is lower than in someone who does not have the condition. There are ways to increase your child's dopamine levels to help them feel better. Some foods have the ability to help your child's brain release this dopamine, such as apples, eggs, leafy green vegetables, and watermelon.

- Stress management: Stress management is critical because stress can be a trigger of ADHD. There are different ways to manage stress appropriately for your child.
- Setting a strict and healthy sleep routine: Never underestimate the power of a healthy sleep routine. Children with many disorders manage their symptoms better when they can truly rest while they sleep. Sleep reduces restlessness and lack of focus. Many children with ADHD find it hard to sleep. If you set a healthy sleep schedule in which your child sleeps at the same time every day and consistently perform a bedtime routine, you can also reduce symptoms. You can have a bedtime routine of bathing, putting on their pajamas, reading a book, then making the room sleep conducive (dark, calm, relaxed, and soothing).
- Exercise: This is an important factor necessary for every child. Give your child time to play and run around with other children, but with supervision to ensure they do not get too stimulated. Exercise is essential for their physical and mental health.
- Meditation and mindfulness: Meditation and mindfulness will train your child's focus and sharpen their awareness. Meditation might also

combat their lack of self-control. The benefits of meditation can significantly reduce the symptoms of ADHD.

- Music therapy: Listening to your favorite music can calm your nerves and brain and help you focus more. Music therapy does not require your child to play an instrument or sing. You can play your child's favorite music to calm their nerves and help them immerse themselves in a task.
- Art therapy: Like music therapy, coloring, drawing, or painting, doing crafts can be calming for children with ADHD. They do not have artistic talents for these activities to help them. The simple act of sitting down to work on them can have calming effects.
- Spending time with your child: No therapies are as effective as quality time. As you spend time with your child, you allow them to loosen up and express their feelings to you. You can do something fun during this time to keep your child engaged. While spending time with them, remember to praise them when you notice positive behavior changes.
- Join support groups: You need support groups to meet other parents like you. Managing your ADHD child can be a long road, and it often

feels lonely and exhausting when you have not met other parents going through the same thing. When you join these support groups, you gain a sense of belonging and new ideas to help you manage your child's disorder.

11

SUPPORT RESOURCES FOR PARENTS

As a parent, living with a child with ADHD can be overwhelming, and sometimes it can feel like there is no way forward, but rest assured, there are several ways you can take control of the situation. You are not alone in this journey; others have gone through what you are going through and are facing what you have to deal with. Numerous resources have been made available to help you navigate your way through this journey. You are not alone in your quest to give your child the best care and attention possible so that they can be happy and successful. Other parents are going through the same things, and they can help you learn about all aspects of your child's ADHD, such as inattentiveness and explosive behaviors. However, you must remember that your child is unique, and what works for one family might not be what works for yours. Similar symptoms of ADHD do not mean that the same action plan will work for your child.

BEST ADHD PODCASTS

Parenting a child with ADHD can keep your hands full all the time and make you wonder if you can ever fully understand your child's struggles. Your busy schedule might hinder you from reading books or doing adequate research, but there is always a solution. One solution is listening to podcasts. You can do this anytime without worrying about it interfering with your busy schedule; while on the go, you can just tune in, and you are good. Via podcasts, you can listen to experts who have substantial knowledge about what you are experiencing and are willing to walk you through this journey. Podcasts are one effective mechanism that can guide you on the right path. Below are several podcasts that focus on different aspects of ADHD.

- Parenting ADHD: This podcast is hosted by Penny Williams, a mother who was prompted to learn more about ADHD when her son was diagnosed. Her topics cover everything a parent needs to know about understanding their children, and her personal experience also makes her discussion relatable.

- Distracted: Podcaster Mark Patey was in fifth grade when he was diagnosed with ADHD. His diagnosis was not a hindrance to him having a bright future, as he went on to become a successful businessman. His show serves as an eye-opener to what it means to live with ADHD.

- ADHD Essentials: This gives the parents blueprints for assisting their child with activities such as homework. Guests on the show range from parents to mental health experts and professionals.

- Adulting With ADHD: After her diagnosis, Sarah Snyder launched this podcast to shed more light on how ADHD affects women, especially regarding hormones. This podcast features women who discuss how they dealt with ADHD during various phases, such as pregnancy and menopause.

- Faster Than Normal: This show shares the accomplishments of people with ADHD. Successful individuals who have become well-known talk about their struggles and how they made a name for themselves despite their diagnosis. The host, Peter Shankman, sees his

ADHD as a gift and is set on making others see the positive side of living with this disorder.

- ADHD reWired: This podcast consists of interviews with professionals in this field and individuals living with ADHD. The discussion is made relatable, and strategies are also disseminated. The host, Eric Tivers, addresses his journey living with ADHD and how he maneuvered his way through life.

- I Have ADHD: The podcaster is an ADHD life coach who has devoted time to assisting people diagnosed with ADHD. She educates them on managing their time effectively and wields their skills. The show also answers questions born out of curiosity and provides guidance on how to live a successful life. She uses her experience to enlighten listeners on the diagnosis and how to live with it.

- ADHD Experts: This podcast from ADDitude has experts with concrete knowledge about ADHD answering questions and passing on information about the medical disorder.

- Hacking Your ADHD: The host, William Curb, advises his listeners on how to deal with the dilemmas of ADHD. His advice comes from his personal experience and information from guests he has on the show.

Listening to the right podcast goes a long way in helping you understand your child better because you have a broader awareness of the challenges they are going through. In addition, hearing from people who understand the situation encourages you to move forward.

BEST ADHD APPS

People diagnosed with ADHD often find it difficult to remember certain things and handle complex activities, which is where ADHD apps come in. The major focus of these apps is to boost the productivity level of the user. ADHD apps can never replace professional health personnel, but they help get chores done. The apps do not remove the symptoms but make you productive and organized. The advancement in technology has had a major role to play in creating an even ground for individuals diagnosed with ADHD, in the sense that it helps them to dig deep into themselves and bring forth their potential. Several apps have been created to this effect and can be customized to suit your needs.

The following list includes some of the best apps:

- RescueTime: This app helps an individual manage time effectively. It keeps track of your activities, allows you to set goals, and tells you how much time you spend on each activity. RescueTime ensures users do not waste time doing unproductive activities by setting limitations. It also has a special feature that measures the user's improvement.
- Dragon: This is an incredible app for taking voice dictation. Rather than typing out your thoughts, all the user has to say aloud is recorded and transcribed into text.
- Headspace: This app encourages meditation and helps to relax the mind. It helps an individual stay calm and focused through guided breathing exercises.
- Trello: This is an app that helps you manage your to-do list. It enables you to organize tasks according to your style. Trello also encourages teamwork by providing the means to collaborate on projects.
- SimpleMind Mind Mapping: This app enables the user to create a map of one's thoughts and ideas. The user can also upload voice

recordings, documents, and other media to back up information, allowing the user to follow their train of thought.

FACEBOOK SUPPORT GROUPS

Much time is devoted to caring for an individual with ADHD, which can hinder physical contact with people with similar experiences. A support group is a community of individuals confronting a common issue and coming together to share what they are going through. It is a safe haven for people to express their sincere emotions about their experiences and learn from the experience of others. ADHD support groups can be via conference calls, in-person meetings, or online forums. Their meetings can either be regular or occasional. An online support group is a great avenue to meet with individuals far and wide who are dealing with ADHD or have loved ones with this diagnosis.

There are numerous support groups on various social media platforms that can provide comfort for you as you tread this path. A social media platform such as Facebook boasts various groups where individuals diagnosed with ADHD or relatives with this medical disorder can share their stories and seek advice. Facebook can be used for several reasons, including obtaining more knowledge about a particular subject matter. There are a ton of educational groups on Facebook that can give you a substantial amount of information and also support you in this journey. Some of these groups are:

- ADDitude ADHD Support Group.
- Parenting a Child with ADHD
- ADHD Diagnosed in Adulthood
- ADHD Meds Question & Support Group
- Unlocking ADHD Support Community
- My Child Has ADHD Support Group

You stand to gain many benefits by joining a Facebook support group as a parent taking care of a child diagnosed with ADHD. The advantages of joining a Facebook support group include the following:

- gaining more information about understanding your child
- creating an avenue for you to share your experience and learn from the experience of others
- getting advice
- being well-informed of the latest studies on how to help your child overcome certain difficulties

- achieving a sense of belonging and avoiding loneliness
- getting exposed to fresh strategies
- engaging in personal growth and development
- developing a feeling of being helpful

TIPS FOR SELF-CARE

The word self-care can be translated to mean caring for yourself. It entails doing things that will keep you healthy in all aspects of your life, physically or spiritually. Tending to a child diagnosed with ADHD can leave you with little to no time to look after yourself and the family. It might occasionally seem like a lot to juggle, leaving you out of touch with things happening around you. Therefore, it also becomes fundamental for you to pay close attention to your well-being because it influences the core of the family. So how do you care for yourself while caring for your child? The following is a list of tips that will point you in the right direction and help you focus on cultivating a healthy lifestyle amidst the fatigue you are experiencing:

- Open communication: Never think that you are alone. Communicate openly, especially with your spouse. Communication is vital in maintaining your well-being, especially mentally. Keeping your feelings and struggles bottled up will eventually take a toll on you. As parents, you need to learn to assist one another and work as a team. Set aside time to discuss what you are going through and what systems can be implemented. Doing this will help you find yourself when you think you cannot go on.

- Daily evaluation: There will be days when it seems like you have gotten to the end of the road and you cannot go further and days when you feel discouraged. Such time is when you focus on the positive aspects of your day rather than dwelling on the negative aspects. At the end of each day, critically consider how to improve what has been done so far. If possible, write it down to remind you of your achievements and what remains to be done. This act will keep you moving forward and help you focus on the positives.

- Realistic expectations: Set feasible goals for both you and those around you. Do not entertain certain expectations merely because they might improve your child's growth and learning. Instead, everything should be done based on your child's pace of understanding. To do this, you need to discern their level of progress, as this will help you generate practical expectations. You set goals for your child as you set them for yourself. Do not try to be a hero and do everything at once, all by yourself. Accept all the help you can get since you can only care for your child when you are in the right frame of mind.

- Positive self-talk: Parenting a child with ADHD can be overwhelming sometimes, making it difficult to maintain a positive attitude. Just as it is crucial to instill good manners in your children by setting an example as a parent, you should also exercise positive self-talk. This is one of the most important parts of self-care. Our thoughts have a way of influencing our actions, so it is paramount that we choose our words and thoughts carefully. We find it difficult to compliment ourselves even when we deserve it, and we are always quick to criticize. Even if something seems like a small win compared to what we envisioned, we should still learn to appreciate it. When you practice positive self-talk, you are relieved from stress, and your outlook on the day is altered positively. Do not be hard on yourself; speak positively and appreciate what you do. Be mindful of how you speak to yourself, and do not be in a hurry to critique yourself.

Compliment yourself from time to time after reflecting on your accomplishments. Daily affirmations can also have a positive effect on your life. They have helped me so much that I created an audiobook for mothers called 'Take a Breath, Mamas.' You can find the book on Audible under Carmen Lyons.

- Time to rest: You might wonder where you will get the time to rest despite being so busy trying to make everything work. There is always time for anything when you consciously try to create time. Spend quality time getting ample sleep. Take a break and get yourself involved in things that interest you. Taking a break does not necessarily mean you have to sleep; you can take a walk or practice yoga. Meditation is a good form of rest, as it helps you find your inner calm. Having your "me" time is vital. You are only helpful to others when you are at your peak level of performance, and this will not be possible if you are strained.

- Professional help: Figuring out a working pattern for you, your child, and the family can be overwhelming, and it is not a journey that should be embarked on independently. Seek professional counsel, as this will equip you with the right insight on what to do and what not to do. Talk to experts who are knowledgeable in this field and can guide you through the necessary steps. One suggestion is to reach out and find a parenting coach. This person should be available to you and can help you create a unique parenting plan that fits your life and your family's needs while also prioritizing your needs.

- Regular exercise: It might seem impossible to find time to exercise, but it is a great stress reliever. It also has a way of making you happy as a result of the endorphins it releases. Remember, you can only care for others effectively when you are best. Exercise does not have to be strenuous— it can be as easy as walking in the park or around the house.
- Fun activities: The definition of fun differs for everyone, but the goal is the same—relaxation. Carve out time to do something you truly love that relaxes you. It can be as simple as picking up a book to read. Only make sure that you do something you relish.
- Quality time with friends and family: Enjoy their company and have solace in companionship despite your busy schedule.

Focusing on yourself does not make you selfish; it will help you maintain a happy home. Seizing time to look after yourself helps you relieve the pressure of your daily activities and reset. One of the advantages of self-care is that it helps you refine your attention and increase your energy level.

CONCLUSION

You are a parent. You have tried everything possible to help your child understand and control their emotions, but they will not listen. You are tired of the fighting, yelling, destructive behavior, and disrespect, and you just want to escape the mess. But remember, your problems will follow you wherever you go. The guilt of not being able to help your child is the worst feeling in the world. The good thing is that help is abundant for those who seek it.

Being diagnosed with ADHD does not hinder your child from being successful or leading an exemplary life. However, as a parent, you must help yourself and your child by keeping your emotions in check. Emotions can claw into your decisions and affect your actions, so you must make time for yourself to unwind.

Work towards bringing out the best in your child. Your support, intentionality, and dedication will shape your child's future and guarantee a good life. Refrain from speaking negatively to your child. Instead, you should build up their confidence with positive words. Avoid using triggering words or phrases that threaten their self-esteem. Your child's success lies in your hands.

The importance of empathy in relationships cannot be overemphasized. We all desire to be loved; the same is true for your child. Treat your child's feelings with the utmost respect, and never disregard how they feel. View your child positively and be determined to see them achieve tremendous accomplishments. ADHD may cause your child to seem detached and lacking in remorse or empathy. However, the truth is that they might be oblivious to the proper ways to conduct themselves in various situations.

This is where you come in as a guide. Children with ADHD often face emotional breakdowns because they have to put in twice the effort other children make to succeed at basic skills. In addition, they are often misunderstood by those ignorant of their medical disorder. As parents who care for individuals diagnosed with ADHD, you must rise and support your child in all situations. This goes a long way to prevent your child from carrying a lifelong stigma that will affect their future. Communicate openly with your child and work together on building self-esteem.

The debate between using medications or alternative therapies for your child can be an intense conflict; nevertheless, it is still subject to the advice of a professional health practitioner. In treating ADHD, stimulant and non-stimulant medicines can be used depending on the child's level of improvement. Using medication as a form of treatment has its benefits and drawbacks, but this does not imply that it should not be used. On the contrary, medicine and therapy will be needed in the long run when treating ADHD. Aside from medications, other methods can be employed, such as psychotherapy, social skills training, parental and teacher training, support groups, etc.

Structure is key to maintaining organization and focus when tending to your child. Creating a daily routine for your child enhances the child's concentration level, which, in turn, yields success. It may take months before the routine can be done without hiccups, so stay vigilant and change what is necessary, but only a little at a time. You should not leave your child to figure things out alone; rather, you should stand as a guide and instructor. As parents, ensure that the structure you have put in place in your home is conducive to your child's development.

With consistent support, proper strategies, and conscious effort, it is possible for a child with ADHD to have a normal school life. First, you must inform the proper authorities of your child's disorder; the rest is as easy as possible. ADHD should not be seen as a hindrance to academic excellence, as it can be managed in a school environment. Promote social activities for your child, give them ways to deflect peer pressure, and help them develop their social skills. The principal element to achieving this is to establish communication. Do not use ADHD as an excuse to seclude your child.

As parents who have to cater to the needs of children with ADHD, you must realize you are not alone in this journey. You do not have to do it all on your own, and several aids have been made available to guide you and provide the knowledge you need to care for your child adequately. You can use resources like podcasts that focus on dealing with ADHD and apps that direct you on what to do next while also paying attention to your child's improvement. In everything you do, remember that others are going through what you are experiencing and understand how you feel. Support groups help you relate with others, which is one of the vital resources you need to maintain your mental and emotional stability.

As a final observation, you must understand the significance of being open to knowledge. Aspire to know more than you already know. Pay close attention to your child's needs, and in the process, do not lose sight of your goal to help your child live a happy, fulfilled, and successful life.

Read this book's chapters, apply them confidently, and see the change yourself. This book explains how you must evaluate your strategies and address your child's issues. Make notes, set reminders, and consistently practice strategies to forge confidence in yourself and your child. Some strategies may work, and some may not. But do not get disheartened. Remember—where there is a will, there is a way!

You have no excuse not to raise an extraordinary child. All the resources you need are here, so do not hesitate to take action! In a few easy steps, find the key to peaceful parenting. Stay determined and optimistic, and you will get through this!

A SHINING OPPORTUNITY TO HELP ANOTHER PARENT

WANT TO HELP OTHERS?

You're doing a remarkable thing, and everything you've learned here will make your journey that little bit easier. Now you have the perfect opportunity to give that chance to other parents!

Simply by leaving your honest opinion of this book on Amazon, you'll show new readers where they can find the guidance they're looking for – no matter how little time they have. Don't have an Amazon account? Please consider leaving a review in Goodreads and sharing in other Facebook Groups to help parents know this is a resource they can't pass up.

Thank you for your support. The parenting journey can feel terribly isolating at times... but when we share information, we see that none of us is really alone.

If you are in the UK, please scan the QR code below to leave your review.

If you are in the US, please scan the QR code below to leave your review.

REFERENCES

Bertin, M. (2022, April 6) *Calm starts at home: How to teach emotional regulation skills.* Additude. https://www.additudemag.com/emotional-regulation-skills-adhd-children/

Carlson, G. (2022, February 9). *A new diagnosis for explosive behavior: The pros and cons of disruptive mood dysregulation disorder.* Child Mind Institute. https://childmind.org/article/a-new-diagnosis-for-explosive-behavior/#:~:text=The%20fact%20is%2C%20you%20get,%2C%20hypersexuality%2C%20and%20disordered%20thinking

Dodson, W. (2022, August 10) *When angry kids lash out: How to defuse explosive reactions.* Additude. https://www.additudemag.com/angry-kids-explosive-emotional-dysregulation-adhd/#:~:text=Create%20a%20Diversion,regain%20a%20sense%20of%20control

Hallowel, E. (2022, April 9). *To master anger, first understand it.* Additude. https://www.additudemag.com/your-add-life-13/

Miller, C. (2022, August 3). How to help children calm down. Child Mind Institute. https://childmind.org/article/how-to-help-children-calm-down/?fbclid=IwAR1vgvR0oPuJyBkM752dVDkxaRd-O0a3iAfhySZH_6LlsAZBm16NwV1tWPM4#

Schuck, P. (2022, March 31). *Why your child's ADHD outbursts are so explosive—and isolating.* Additude. https://www.google.com/amp/s/www.additudemag.com/outbursts-in-adhd-children/amp/